The Black Lace
Sexy
Quiz
Book

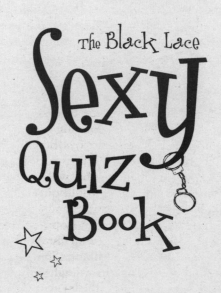

The Black Lace

Sexy Quiz Book

BLACK LACE   Maddie Saxon

First published in 2004
by Black Lace
Thames Wharf Studios
Rainville Road
London
W6 9HA

A catalogue record for this book is available from the British Library.

ISBN 0 352 33884 9

Typeset by TW Typesetting, Plymouth, Devon
Printed and bound by Mackays of Chatham PLC

CONTENTS

Introduction   1

1. YOUR PERSONALITY TYPE   7

Introverts and Extraverts ● Are You an Extravert or an Introvert?
● Intuitive or Sensation Types ● Are You an Intuitive or Sensation
Type? ● Thinking or Feeling Types ● Are You a Thinking or
Feeling Type? ● Identifiying Your Sexual Personality Type

2. YOUR SEXUAL CHARACTER   33

What Flavour is Your Sexuality? ● How Sexually Confident Are
You? ● Maddie's Sexual Confidence Masterclass

3. DATING AND RELATING   65

What Sexual Signals Are You Giving Out? ● Ten Tips For
Meeting People ● Ten Tips For Good Flirting ● Ten Tips For
Looking Effortlessly Sexy ● Body Talk ● Body Language Secrets ●
What Does Your Date's Body Language Say to You?

4. YOUR SEXUAL PSYCHE   91

Growing Up in the Commercial Age ● How Has Your Sexual
Psyche Evolved? ● Our Changing Psyche

5. YOUR SEXUAL IMAGINATION   103

The Persona and the Personal Unconscious ● Exploring Fantasy
Archetypes ● What Are Your Favourite Archetypes?

6. EXPLORING SEXUAL NARRATIVES   131

Seven Sample Fantasies and What They Mean

7. GETTING DOWN TO IT   145

How Sexually Opportunistic Are You? ● How Sexually
Adventurous Are You? ● How Kinky Are You? ● Survival Pack
for Sexual Adventurers ● Is it Love or Lust?

8. THE BIG O   171

Orgasm Mysteries, Problems and Solutions

9. MADDIE'S SEX AND RELATIONSHIPS
SURVIVAL GUIDE   183

How Healthy Is Your Relationship? ● Ten Tough Relationship
Questions ● Have a Relationship Review ● The Green-eyed
Monster ● Green-eye Solutions ● How to Spot a Dysfunctional
Lover – 25 Warning Signs ● The Way to Healthy Relationships

INTRODUCTION

There are few experiences that quicken the heart, up the body temperature or excite the imagination as potently as the thrill of sexual congress. Whether you are in the early stages of flirting with someone who has just begun to arouse your interest, or are having regular, full-blown sessions of steamy lovemaking with a long-term partner, you'll know that exercising the sexual part of ourselves feels good. The energy exchange that comes about when two adults share mutual sexual attraction is a truly uplifting tonic – you suddenly get a spring in your step and feel more aware of your body and the image you are projecting of yourself; it's as if everything around you is more colourful and vibrant.

The theme of chase and capture is an enduring one. Since the dawn of civilisation, the story of being sexually enraptured by another has been a universal theme, and since humans were first able to make a mark, sexual conquest has been a dominant motif. We've been having sex for some two million years, and it's safe to assume that it is very popular. In many ways it is the essential human drive. It gives purpose to life, allowing us to know exquisite pleasure while ensuring the continuation of the species. As a design mechanism it's been a winner.

Recent tests have proven that regular sex boosts the immune system; that wonderful post-orgasmic endorphin rush is nature's great legal high. There's no comedown, it's free, and, unlike drugs or alcohol, it is extremely beneficial to our sense of well-being. The regular release of endorphins into our spinal fluid at the moment of orgasm is said to help us deal with stress and promote healthy sleep patterns. Sex can make us feel great. In this aspect, it's all good news – providing we keep it safe, of course, and do not expose ourselves to sexually transmitted diseases.

Most people will admit to enjoying regular sex, and no one likes to think of themselves as a lousy lover. Therefore, the whole business of satisfying our need for regular love action should be a breeze, if we all basically want the same thing, right? Unfortunately this does not seem to be the case. Along with the great thrills to be found through sexual relationships come frequent disappointments, misunderstandings and incompatibilities. Our sexuality is hot-wired to the most fragile part of us – our ego – and we can easily find ourselves mentally bruised and sulking when a partner forgets to accord us the attention we need. We are also harsher with our lovers than we ever are with our friends. We expect so much from them, upping the stakes the longer we are together. We are conditioned into progressing our relationships along a linear path that moves from the carefree 'going out' stage through to the responsibility of living together or getting married and then buying property and having children – all very expensive and requiring huge commitment. Bogged down by practicalities, many of us can find that somewhere along the line our sexy side has faded into obscurity when what we should be doing is preserving and nurturing that playful, life-enhancing aspect of our lives.

Our friendships don't get put through the emotional wringer in the way our partnerships do. When was the last time we sat down with our best friend and attempted to discuss where that friendship was going? This is because, you will say, we don't have sex with our friends. At least, most of us don't, and this is precisely the point.

Sex ups the ante. Those with whom we have a sexual relationship have access to the most private aspect of our psyches – putting it bluntly, the psychological processes that enable us to orgasm – and nothing is more personal than that. Human beings – complex, intelligent creatures, defined alone by the unique ability of language – are brought to orgasm by the intellectual as much as physiological. This is particularly true for women, for whom fantasies are often essential in order for them to climax.

Orgasm can be triggered by the curious, the intangible, the embarrassing, the outlandish and even the politically incorrect – stuff we are unlikely to confess to our friends. If we want our partners to satisfy us, we need to trust them with our 'sexual profile' – our blueprint for personal pleasure – however bizarre it may be. When we see couples out at parties, clubs and bars – or even out shopping – it is fascinating to think that each of them is carrying around the details of their partner's sexual fantasies and the particular physical quirks that make them climax. And what a potentially explosive cache of information this is to have about another person! Few of us relish the thought that the details of our erotic imagination could be made public by an ex-partner. Consequently, we need to put a good amount of trust into the people with whom we have sex. We can get caught in a double bind: in order to enjoy fulfilling relationships, it is important that our partners know what arouses us. Yet often a breakdown of communication due to shyness, or an unwillingness to let our secret selves be known, means that couples get stuck, each having silent, guilty desires they are too embarrassed to share, when they could be having so much fun *together*. As we can see, the carefree thrills of the first stirrings of sexual attraction can easily turn into communication breakdown.

As a sex therapist, I have had countless conversations with women who have fantastic erotic fantasies and highly complex requirements for orgasm – yet almost all will speak about themselves as 'weird' or 'not normal'. Then there are the many others who find it difficult to admit to what they really want in the bedroom. Despite a wealth of good books being available about sexual fantasy, it is still natural to be shy of discussing what we like individually, or what we think about when we masturbate. In our hectic world, we work long hours and maintain high-octane social lives, as well as trying to keep control of our domestic affairs, so it can seem more appealing to flop in front of the TV rather than make time to unlock the mystery of our inner selves. Yet by ignoring our sexual psychology we could be missing out on a more rewarding life. Many of us take our sexual feelings for granted, knowing what we like yet not analysing them or discussing them openly. This is particularly true for men.

But if you want to know more about your secret self and be better equipped to satisfy yourself and your lover, then the *Black Lace Sexy Quiz Book* is a great place to start unlocking those mysteries. The quizzes cover the many facets of the mysterious and beguiling inner world of attraction, desire and sexual fantasy. Some questions ask us about our behaviour in social situations – from the hit and miss circus of the dating game, knowing whether it's love or lust, right through to working out what your body language is saying. Other questions are more light-hearted, probing into our tastes when it comes to style, movies and clothes – and all the things that contribute to the image we project to potential lovers. Other sections will provide you with the tools you need to identify what may be going wrong in your relationship and the psychological blockages that may be preventing you from having the kind of sex life you dream about. Most importantly, after answering all the questions in this book, you will have your own Personal Sexual Profile.

By undertaking self-analysis, we can learn more about our sexuality than if we leave it to chance discovery. Sex is the way through which many of us express and satisfy the emotions and feelings associated with other needs in our lives. By rating your secret sexual self and identifying your sexual type – and the types you are attracted to – you can begin to feel more confident about discussing with others what you really want and what turns you on. The key to getting the most out of this book is to undertake an honest self-assessment. As you work through each section, you may want to keep the analysis in a private notebook, rather than mark the actual book. You most likely do not want your friends reading what you have ticked! Write down on a separate piece of paper the question number and answer number. When you have answered all the questions in a particular survey, turn to the end of the section and read the analysis. Remember, there is no 'wrong' answer. This is not an exam. The only thing to promise is that you will answer the questions honestly and try not to predict the outcome. No one is going to see your answers but yourself. There is only you and your honest replies!

Don't try answering the questions sitting on a crowded train or while there are lots of noisy distractions. All the quizzes are best done alone, in a private space such as your bedroom, or somewhere peaceful where you can let your mind be free to explore your inner self. Don't answer the questions in front of friends or your partner, as this can encourage you to tick an answer you may want others to think is really 'you' but is not the real answer. We all project a persona onto those around us, but this book is about finding the inner person –

no cheating! So relax, get into the flow of the questions, and open up the doorway to your most private and exciting inner self!

1. YOUR PERSONALITY TYPE

This first section is all about YOU. It is where you will identify your basic Personality Type and begin to create a profile of your character. Once we have determined this, we will then move on to the more personal stuff of how we form sexual partnerships, how we relate in bed and what our fantasies reveal. Throughout the book we will be exploring the juicy detail of your sexual psyche in all its wild and wonderful glory, and finding out what really makes you tick. There will be features on sexual self-confidence and a survival guide for modern relationships, as well as plenty of hot tips to ensure your love life reaches its sizzling potential and stays on course. But, to begin with, we are going to peel away the first layer of your persona and find out what type of person you are underneath the face that you present to the world. Although this first set of questions is not concerned with sexual behaviour as such, it is nonetheless important because this is where you will draw the framework that will be the basis for your personal character profile. The content will hot up soon enough, so enjoy this 'temperate' introductory section as the gateway to a much steamier place!

It was the eminent twentieth-century psychologist Carl Gustav Jung who first formulated the concept of Personality Types. He was fascinated by the unconscious and by dreams, and the fact that human behaviour seems to follow certain basic patterns. Everyone has heard of introverts and extraverts – the words now form part of everyday language – yet they were not used before Jung.

He divided these two main personality types into a further four categories based on how we function. His observation was that behavioural traits operate as pairs of opposites: thinking or feeling; intuition or experience, etc. He thought that during the course of a person's development one of each 'pair' becomes preferred, resulting in characteristic behaviour that becomes predictable. If we think of friends or members of our family, we can take a good guess as to how each person will react to a set of circumstances. This is due to their predominant Personality Type. It is the exception that proves the rule; think of how it always throws us off guard when someone 'goes against type'.

Of course, we all develop habitual, individual sexual behaviour too – tending to interact with sexual partners in preferred learned ways – from the early stages of flirting, right through to how we perform in the heat of the moment. There are also recognisable Sexual Personality Types, whom we will identify in the next chapter, along with 'archetypes' – another Jungian concept that is extremely useful in analyzing sexual fantasies: why we are attracted to certain characters (real and imagined), and what kinds of physical and psychological types catch our eye and even provoke instant arousal. For now, though, let's lay the foundations of your character type.

INTROVERTS AND EXTRAVERTS

We live in a society that rewards extraverts, and we have come to believe – somewhat unfairly – that being an extravert is the 'better' condition. Extraverts are the people who are perceived as being the achievers, primarily because they are more disposed to talking about themselves and making contact with others. Hence, life tends to move more quickly for extraverts. They are the ones who enjoy team sports at school, or who volunteer to partake in or organise activities that involve communication and showmanship. The Western world in general is a very extravert civilisation, built on conquering, exploring, building and trading. Consequently, people who display the same character traits as the dominant culture find it easier to slot into the life patterns that the prevailing society holds up as the ideal model.

Introverts, however, are the ones whose brains and hard work results in great discovery. They are often the designers, the planners, the thinkers and inventors – those people for whom the phrase 'still waters run deep' was coined. They may not be as boastful or as entertaining at dinner parties, but they often have the better imaginations. Many introverts are writers, composers and artists. When we think of all the products we love to use, or that make our lives easier, such as computer games, DVD players, cars, washing machines and the Internet, it was most likely an introvert who was responsible for designing it or making it available for our consumption. The Eastern world traditionally values introversion, where stillness, reflection, meditation and elegance are prized over combativeness and achievement. But the ideal situation is a mixture of both – one of balance and harmony.

What follows is the most basic Jungian Typology test. Remember that introverts are no less 'sexy' than their extravert friends; it's just that they approach the whole process of seduction and arousal from different perspectives. The sexy studious librarian or secretary will be sizzling with as much passion beneath the surface as the lap-dancing showgirl displays up-front. And don't write off that guy with the glasses in the accounts department; he can be just as horny as the sports hero, it's just that he's not 'announcing' it with his body.

These first quizzes will enable you to identify whether you are *primarily* an introvert or extravert. Few people are totally one type. But if you are, then you may be a little out of balance. A completely extravert character can be something of a nightmare for others. It's the person who will never shut up on the night bus, or the 'me first' type who barges to the head of the queue. Conversely, total introverts will find it very difficult to realise their desires. We have to interact with others in society, no matter how unpalatable this may seem. The total introvert may miss out on a lot of the fun of life – which keeps us happy and 'in the loop' – and their talent and what they have to offer may not get the chance to benefit everyone else. Total introverts appear to have something of a sad soul because they will be out of kilter with the dominant culture in which they live.

Remember: the ideal is always balance and harmony.

ARE YOU AN EXTRAVERT OR AN INTROVERT?

Q. 1 – At parties where you don't know many people, are you usually:

(a) a good mingler

(b) rather shy, wanting others to speak to you first

Q. 2 – The office party demands fancy dress. Do you:

(a) start thinking immediately what costume you are going to wear

(b) groan inwardly and know you'll feel uncomfortable joining in

Q. 3 – You have to make an informal speech to a group of colleagues. Do you:

(a) ad lib as you go. You like to think on your feet as that makes you appear more spontaneous

(b) plan what you are going say, preparing notes that you can refer to, in case you lose your flow

Q. 4 – Do you like to spend your free time:

(a) actively socialising where you could meet a sexy new partner

(b) reading, listening to music or dreaming of your ideal romance

Q. 5 – Do group discussions with friends or colleagues:

(a) stimulate you and give you energy

(b) make you feel nervous

Q. 6 – When in a group, how do you react to a sudden event: the telephone ringing or an unexpected question?

(a) leap up or respond immediately

(b) wait for someone else to deal with it

Q. 7 – Which do you prefer?

(a) having a wide circle of acquaintances

(b) a few close friends

Q. 8 – In group situations in which other people are directly involved, do you prefer:

(a) being at the centre of events

(b) going with the flow

Q. 9 – You are in a restaurant or bar with a group of five or more people, do you:

(a) join in the general conversation

(b) talk with one person at a time

Q. 10 – Again, in social situations are you more likely to:

(a) introduce people

(b) get introduced

Q. 11 – When new people meet you, do they find out your interests:

(a) quickly

(b) only once they get to know you better

Q. 12 – Do you get more pleasure from:

(a) shopping with friends and chatting on the way

(b) solitary walks where you can think about stuff

Q. 13 – Are you more of a:

(a) speaker

(b) listener

Q. 14 – Do you express yourself more clearly:

(a) in conversation

(b) in writing

Q. 15 – The seat next to you on the plane is empty. Do you:

(a) hope someone cool and sexy will sit in it

(b) hope it stays that way

Q. 16 – Do you chat easily with cab drivers, hairdressers, etc.?

(a) yes, you actively enjoy it and you can have a laugh

(b) no, you prefer not to share your business with strangers

Q. 17 – Assuming you like both types of person, would you generally prefer to spend time with:

(a) lively people

(b) reflective people

Q. 18 – Do you tend to develop:

(a) your outer life (sports, parties, socialising)

(b) your inner life (reading, meditating, dreaming)

Q. 19 – Do you like to be occupied by:

(a) a variety of tasks

(b) one thing at a time

Q. 20 – Do you prefer to:

(a) hear about an event

(b) read about an event

Now calculate how many questions you answered (a) and how many you answered (b). Make a note of your (a) and (b) scores and keep them for later, when we will plot your introversion/extraversion rating on the chart. Most people have one basic type that is predominant. A few will be positioned right in the middle. There is nothing 'wrong' if you get a score of 10 a's and 10 b's. This simply means that you are very balanced and are not easily defined as one particular type. The next set of questions will probe a little deeper, and is about how you perceive the world around you, and how you acquire information.

INTUITIVE OR SENSATION TYPES

This is a pair of opposites that determines how we make sense of the world and how we perceive experiences.

The intuitive type works on hunches about things, and tends to function 'organically', simultaneously being aware of all the possibilities and outcomes of a situation: the future, the past and the present. They are not practical in their application, tending to avoid detail and the monotonous regularities that are an unfortunate part of life. Intuitive types are interested in the meanings, relationships and possibilities between people that go beyond what you can experience through your immediate senses. They look at the big picture and try to find overall patterns. They are innovative and value imagination and inspiration beyond factual knowledge. This type has the potential to be truly visionary and can bring creative flair – if not always diligence – to a particular project.

The sensation type is better understood as an 'experience' type. The word sensation here does not mean thrill-seeking; it merely refers to sensory impressions – how things look and feel and 'really are'. Sensation types are grounded individuals who do not have much time for the 'what ifs' of life. They look at the realities of a situation. They are good at working in the here and now, and with the tools of a given situation. They are realistic and practical. They are good at remembering facts and how things work. They like to stick to proven methods and are particular about detail. They get on and do a job according to what it requires. The advantage of being a sensation type is not being bogged down by projecting into the future, and wondering what may go wrong, which the introverted intuitive type is prone to doing. The sensation type will want the facts, just the facts.

ARE YOU AN INTUITIVE OR SENSATION TYPE?

Q. 1 – For social events, would you describe yourself as:

(a) casual

(b) punctual

Q. 2 – In assessing the quality of something or someone (such as a potential new lover), is your first reaction to:

(a) assess the overall picture (personality, feeling)

(b) look at the details (shoes, nails, hair)

Q. 3 – On holiday, do you act mostly on:

(a) the spur of the moment (depending on your mood or who's asking!)

(b) according to plan (you like to know what's going to happen)

Q. 4 – Do you tend to:

(a) spend (you can't resist a bargain)

(b) save (you never know when you may be faced with a large bill)

Q. 5 – Does keeping things orderly:

(a) become a real bother

(b) come naturally

Q. 6 – When you are about to travel do you:

(a) pack at the last minute, scattering frilly items all around your bedroom

(b) pack methodically, at leisure, neatly folding dry-cleaned, pressed outfits

Q. 7 – Do you overlook details because of pressing interests and diversions?

(a) often (you always think about many things at once)

(b) seldom (you prefer to compartmentalise your thinking)

Q. 8 – When a book is disappointing do you:

(a) leave it and begin another (life's too short!)

(b) finish it anyway (you hate unfinished business)

Q. 9 – Do you reach conclusions:

(a) by inspiration

(b) by calculation and plan

Q. 10 – If living alone, do you:

(a) not bother much with neatness

(b) keep things in precise order

Q. 11 – Are you tempted to new pursuits:

(a) often (you never know who you may meet)

(b) never (you like to stick to what you are good at)

Q. 12 – Are you restless for no good reason:

(a) never (you're so laid back you can chill out anywhere, anytime)

(b) often (you often feel you're missing out on something)

Q. 13 – When shopping for a present do you:

(a) pick something that will be a surprise (you love getting a reaction)

(b) pick something you know the person will want (you like to please)

Q. 14 – Having formed an opinion about someone do you:

(a) happily alter it

(b) stick to it steadfastly

Q. 15 – Thinking of the future do you:

(a) cross bridges as they come

(b) plan for future contingencies

Q. 16 – Assuming you could earn a living from either, would you prefer:

(a) a creative career

(b) a useful career

Q. 17 – Is neatness in you:

(a) an achievement

(b) inborn

Q. 18 – Do you prefer reading:

(a) fantasy, escapism

(b) current events, rooted in real life

Q. 19 – Do you feel you can judge a person's character on the basis of a brief meeting?

(a) Yes

(b) No

Q. 20 – You are facing a landscape. Are you aware mostly of:

(a) the general shape and colour

(b) the details of buildings, trees, roads, etc.

Again, total up the number of (a) and (b) answers and note them down for the end of this section. There is one more batch of twenty questions, and this will determine whether you are mostly a thinking or feeling type.

THINKING OR FEELING TYPES

Thinking types are objective and try to not let emotions rule their analysis of a situation. They like evidence rather than speculation. They think through the logical consequences of any choice and are good at working out what is wrong with something. They don't feel comfortable with emotionally intense people, and prefer calm rational reactions to passionate ones. They are great at negotiating their way through difficulties by relying on logic. This doesn't mean that thinking types cannot be sensitive; they just prefer to interpret information and carry out tasks by using intellect rather than emotion. This can make them seem rather aloof.

Feeling types make decisions based on what they feel is right for the people concerned. They like harmony and go out of their way to avoid conflict. They are always assessing what effects their decisions will have on others and are sympathetic, appreciative and tactful. They have a strong sense of traditional values and human relationships are important to them. They take an interest in the person behind a project or idea and enjoy pleasing people.

ARE YOU A THINKING OR FEELING TYPE?

Q. 1 – Faced with a friend's distress is your first reaction to:

   (a) determine the cause (it's bound to be about a bloke)

   (b) comfort them (it's bound to be about a bloke)

Q. 2 – When you overhear two people having an argument, do you wish:

   (a) they would reach an amicable agreement (life's too short for arguments)

   (b) they would stop (it upsets you)

Q. 3 – Do you find it easier to devote your energy to

   (a) social problems (environmental, world poverty, etc.)

   (b) friends' problems (boyfriend trouble, nagging parents, etc.)

Q. 4 – When reading, do you prefer:

   (a) biographies (it's good to read inspiring life stories)

   (b) novels (you love to lose yourself in fantasy)

Q. 5 – When your opinions differ considerably from those of your circle do you feel:

- (a) intrigued (especially when you fancy someone that makes them go 'Yuk!')
- (b) uncomfortable (you want their approval)

Q. 6 – When working towards a goal (such as seducing a new guy) are you:

- (a) tenacious – you want him and you're going to get him
- (b) easily put off by other factors, such as his luscious girl mates

Q. 7 – When forming opinions, do you:

- (a) explore others' opinions and look for objectives
- (b) rely exclusively on your personal valuation

Q. 8 – When you see something you think is unfair happening, is your natural response to:

- (a) remain non-committal until you know the facts
- (b) speak out

Q. 9 – When you meet a new guy, do you prefer to talk about:

- (a) his job
- (b) his personal tastes

Q. 10 – Do you usually value:

- (a) logic over sentiment
- (b) sentiment over logic

Q. 11 – Do you think it's more of a compliment to say someone has:
- (a) wit and intelligence
- (b) warmth and humanity

Q. 12 – Do emotional people make you feel:
- (a) nervous in case they 'go off on one'
- (b) inspired by their passion

Q. 13 – Do you like to take your meals:
- (a) at set times
- (b) when you feel like it

Q. 14 – Do you like making lists or collecting stuff?
- (a) yes
- (b) not really

Q. 15 – Are you more interested in people's:
- (a) beliefs
- (b) behaviour

Q. 16 – When you are planning a holiday, do you select from choices:
- (a) you know you can afford, and work from the options
- (b) you dream of going to, and work back from there

Q. 17 – When shopping for new clothes, do you:
- (a) head only for shops within your budget
- (b) window-shop in places you can't afford

Q. 18 – Do you cry at movies?

(a) rarely

(b) often

Q. 19 – Which of these is the worst?

(a) irresponsibility

(b) injustice

Q. 20 – Do you prefer music that is:

(a) instrumental

(b) lyrical

OK, now total up the number of (a) and (b) scores in this last section and you will be ready to plot all of your results on the Typology Graph.

IDENTIFYING YOUR SEXUAL PERSONALITY TYPE

Extravert or Introvert

Note the number from 1–20 of (a) or (b) questions that form the majority of your answers. If, for example you answered 12 a's, which is the extravert category, you leave your 8b answers aside and mark where the number 12 appears on the line that runs Ext–Int.

Intuitive or Sensing

Same again. Note the majority number and mark it on the oblique line that bisects the chart on the line S–I.

Thinking or Feeling

As above. Mark on the line T–F

Now you will be able to determine what three-part type you are. If you want to read more about the basic Personality Type test, there are many books that go into

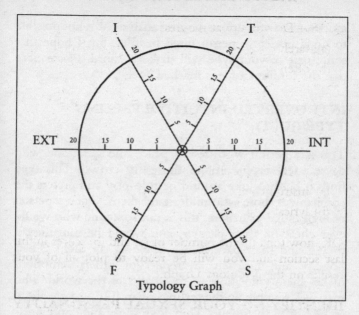

Typology Graph

Jungian Depth Psychology, or you can investigate the Myers Briggs Indicator – a personality profiling tool used by management consultants and major corporations to assess their employees' strengths and weaknesses. The test is extensive and costly, but fantastically interesting, and can be done online. For the purposes of this book, however, we want to place the emphasis on the sexual interpretation of the personality type rather than how you perform in the workplace. Below are six variable types, with each analysis covering the personal aspects of character: basic typology, sexuality and the dark side – the 'shadow' part of the personality. Jung did not apply his typology test to sexuality in the way I am using it for the purposes of this book. The expansion I am using here is original and not part of the theory used in Analytical Psychology. The following categories are meant as a guide only; without one-to-one analysis, it is not possible to draw in-depth, personalised profiles, but I hope that some part of your type will strike a chord. Please note that the Intuitive type is marked as 'U'.

INTROVERTED INTUITIVE FEELING TYPE (IUFT)

This is a person who desires peace and quiet and who doesn't feel happy among the party crowd. This type finds it hard to joke around or role-play and prefers the company of those who understand them. Often a person of high moral principles, this is not someone who would ever cheat on their partner, and would be mortified if they found their partner was cheating on them. Their honesty and heartfelt awareness of others' emotions makes them vulnerable to the sharks of the world, who may well trample on the feelings of an IUFT to get ahead or be first in the queue. They love study and contemplation and will often be good writers.

IUFT's Sexuality

Where this type comes into her own is in the realm of the imagination. While she is not happy in a dominant role and can lack the confidence to chat up strangers, once she has attracted the attention of a possible lover she is able to weave an enchanting spell over him. She has extraordinarily colourful fantasies and daydreams, and her fluid sensuality can appear very feminine and beguiling. This type of woman can be dreamy, warm-hearted and nature-loving and is often attracted to myths and legends and historical drama. She is keen to please, and will spend hours making sure her environment is conducive to languid loving. Once she has woven a web of desire, she is determined that her man stays faithful. But she will not tolerate love at any price. If her man starts acting like an oaf, he will not be welcome in her refined boudoir.

IUFT's Dark Side

Her dark side is one of repressed anger and emotion. As she doesn't voice her opinions as loudly as her extravert sisters, she keeps her feelings bottled up – and that can mean they turn poisonous and vengeful. Colleagues or rivals may think she is a pushover, too mouse-like to fight back. Yet she may harbour revenge fantasies that are ten times scarier than anything her adversaries can conjure up. She can take criticism too much to heart – never seeing it as merely someone else's opinion, but as a wounding blade that pierces her very core. Sexually, her dark side can manifest itself through martyrdom – a longing to be punished or to punish others. Her sexual imagination may create a gothic world of dungeons and castles, dark vampiric figures and demons. She is very likely at some point to be attracted to fetishistic or sado-masochistic activities. If she can keep this side of her sexuality playful and learn to come out of her shell, she will realise that things are only as serious as she allows them to be.

INTROVERTED SENSING FEELING TYPE

ISFTs tend towards being conservative and modest. Usually they do not care to lead a group but are often loyal followers. They hate to be rushed into anything because they might overlook details. They prefer a calm and civilised approach to all things. They never force their opinions or values onto others, although they remain suspicious of other people's motivations, quietly judging and assessing situations according to their own experience. They can sometimes forget to look at the bigger picture, or find it difficult to express themselves. This is a person who likes to plan and be prepared, not someone who is given over to spontaneity and wild abandon. However, such a person is very trustworthy, and is often found working in roles requiring tact, precision and composure.

ISFT's Sexuality

ISFT woman is usually elegant and concerned with looking good. She loves the process of seduction and enjoys building sexual tension to an explosive degree. This is so she can be sure she is wanted. She is the one who will flash just enough leg to get noticed, but who would quickly say she never meant to tease, if she goes off the idea. She is extremely fussy, and her love of detail can stop a budding relationship dead in its tracks if she suddenly decides a guy's clothes or tastes are not to her liking. She likes a man to work hard for her affections, although her remoteness will make her appear as a sexual challenge − an enigma wrapped up in a mystery.

ISFT's Dark Side

She can be so caught up in her own preconceived ideas about people that she cannot see the facts of a matter. She may miss the evidence that a person fancies her, if for some reason, she has convinced herself that it's not to be. But her darkest side lies in her tendency to mistrust people, and this can lead to jealousy or brooding suspicion that something is going on behind her back. She is extremely wary of being taken for granted by her lovers, and will often employ a reserved persona rather than let herself go. She has deep emotions, but if she can learn to believe that it's safe to go wild occasionally, she can be capable of fantastically passionate lovemaking. Whilst she is not about to give her all at anyone else's command, she very much likes seeing the man perform for her. As there is always something secretive about her, it is easy for her lovers to become spellbound, as they cannot resist investigating her mysterious sensuality.

INTROVERTED SENSATION THINKING TYPE

This is someone who wants to know the how and why of everything; who is interested in ideas over facts, although the sensation part of the profile lends them a degree of practicality. This is the personality type associated with the inventor, philosopher, scientist or academic. This person is a cool character who analyses life with a detached curiosity. Such a person may become infatuated with originality, regarding external matter merely as stuff to bolster their own theories. Their minds are always on the go, and they are rarely content to accept things how they are, preferring to see how situations can be improved upon. They have much to offer the world, but must avoid becoming hypercritical.

IST's Sexuality

This is the profile of the 'sexy librarian' type. Although she prefers intellect over emotion, once she is enthusiastic about a lover, she has the potential to become the hottest thing on two legs! Get her in bed and she is inventive and original, although she may be more concerned with her own pleasure than her partner's. Her fantasies may, like her, have an air of cool detachment, being set in sterile offices or boardrooms or the back of a diplomat's car. This type is attracted to quick-witted, bright and rational characters over the more primal, earthy male. She wants intelligent conversation as a prelude to seduction. She is impressed by achievement, is turned on by a wicked sense of humour and looks for a man who is as discriminating about things as she is.

IST's Dark Side

Her dark side is egotistical and easily infatuated – mostly with herself or the wacky ideas she formulates on a whim. She is very much the centre of her universe, and her aloofness may translate as narcissism. She may have more sex toys than the average woman, but will be reluctant to use them in front of a lover. Her sexuality can be somewhat controlling in a quiet, manipulative way, and men of an inferior intellect to hers will be in for a rough ride as she will run rings around them. She has a tendency to use men as a means to an end, but they won't usually complain because her cool approach to sex may be admired by guys who find an overly emotional woman a turn-off. IST is the opposite of clingy. After sex, she may be planning her next big scheme, or will be wrapped up in her own ideas of grandeur.

EXTRAVERTED SENSING THINKING TYPE

Make way for the person who is determined to achieve success; who won't let emotions or self-doubt enter their heads unless they have really overstepped the mark and get told off for it. This is the profile of an objective but materialistic person who doesn't have much truck with sentiment and cannot understand hesitation or procrastination – which will drive them to distraction. This is someone who is very much 'in the real world' and isn't enamoured of dreams or fantasies. They like action and results, make good sports people, and generally can be competitive at the drop of a hat. These people are often the engines that push others along to achieve a team goal. They give their all, and enjoy the praise and success that comes as a result.

EST's Sexuality

They want lots of it, and they want it now. They have a robust attitude to sex and are always keeping one eye out for the next good-looking conquest. If young, they get bored easily, and like to notch up the numbers and gain experience. Once older they are more faithful, but might hook up with a much younger partner who will keep them in the centre of the action. Their sexuality is lively and zesty. They like showmanship and agility, and tend to be the ones to go for unusual sex positions or erotic gymnastics. Tending towards being the dominant partner in the bedroom, it is they who will call the shots. ESTs like looking and performing. EST men will enjoy lap-dancing clubs and sexy clothing; EST women like showing off their assets and dressing up for sex. They leave no doubt as to their intentions when flirting, and have tremendous energy for bedroom antics.

EST's Dark Side

You guessed it: too bossy. Everything is a means to her end, and EST can value sexual quantity over quality. The problem with sensation-type extraverts is they are not the most imaginative or sensitive lovers, going at it like a bull at a gate if a man, and homing in for the lunch box too soon if a woman – which can put some men off. They fling it about on the dance floor in an exhibition of stamina and bravado, and will be the ones wearing the lowest-cut top or the showiest thong. With her sense of the visual, she will be aware of the power she has over men, and will be ruthless in the use of her body to capture her man – even if he is someone else's. She may ride roughshod over people's feelings in order to satisfy her appetite for lusty conquest. In the bedroom she will be demanding and dirty!

EXTRAVERTED INTUITIVE THINKING TYPE

Here's an interesting mixture: outgoing and fun-loving but also creative and thoughtful. They are possibly the best judge of character of all the personality types, and will spot instantly whether a person is genuine or not. They have an inbuilt bullshit detector that will protect them in times of trouble. EUTs see the world as a mass of possibilities, and will love travel and spontaneity, although may zip from enthusiasm to enthusiasm without seeing something through to its conclusion. They can be exasperating in that they are inconsistent and sometimes combative, lacking direction if their thinking part isn't as developed as their intuitive part. They make brilliant actors or performers.

EUT's Sexuality

Expect the unexpected. This type is deeply in touch with her unconscious, and loves all things fantastic and imaginative. As a child she will have been happy exploring her inner world, and as an adult she gets a real kick out of grown-up fantasy worlds. She is fascinated by the subtleties of eroticism. She loves intellectual sexy mind games, and will get huge enjoyment from adopting a number of sexual personae and pretending to be someone other than her real self. In fact, it is sometimes hard to tell who she really is at all. This is the personality most into role-play and dressing up, being something of a natural actor or mimic. Her constant fascination with the new and different can lead her to hop from one lover to the next.

EUT's Dark Side

She is not naturally the most loyal of partners, believing that it is not possible to get everything from one person. She has a fixed idea of what turns her on, and is reluctant to compromise and accommodate her partners' needs. She needs lots of feedback and praise at how exciting she is to be with. Sex tends to be on her terms or not at all. She may be attracted to sexual partners who are irresponsible adventurers, and she is so immersed in wanting to play a role well that she may not realise when she is exposing herself to intense situations that may go too far. She has a fascination for sex with strangers and may be tempted by a lesbian affair just for the display or glamour of it. Her good judge of character protects her from exploitation, but she is prone to taking risks. She should be careful to separate the real person from the (often shocking) personas she enjoys playing.

EXTRAVERTED INTUITIVE FEELING TYPE

This personality type is mostly re-active to the approval of others. They are outgoing, but always put others first, often working in the caring professions such as charities or teaching. They are so keen to create a harmonious environment that they can neglect their own needs. They are the hosts who will put themselves out to ensure their guests have a good time, and will never willingly step on anyone's toes. They worry about what people are thinking, if they are happy, and what they can do to help improve a situation. Whilst they are talkative and sociable, they can dwell on things going wrong more often than right.

EUF's Sexuality

She likes to please. Boy, does she like to please! This is the personality profile of the geisha or courtesan. She loves nothing more than to worship her man and feel that she is providing him with the old-fashioned attention most women find exhausting. She gets pleasure through pleasing others, so she may neglect her own orgasm (or fake it) so long as the man is happy. She will spend ages on perfecting techniques, such as oral sex, and loves to massage her man, enjoying sensuality more than raw passion. She tends towards a holistic sexual approach, seeking a harmonious union of male and female 'energies'. She is likely to be attracted to yoga, tantric sex or Kama Sutra and has a delicate, feminine eroticism.

EUF's Dark Side

I'm afraid that EUF can be a little clingy. She is the type of person who will take on a difficult man, believing that she can change him. Her friends get exasperated by her charitable sexuality. She's the one who will give the ugly bloke a mercy shag, or fail to speak up when she's not being satisfied. Men can easily take her hospitality for granted and, if she doesn't allow herself the gift of sexual self-preservation, she will feel a little let down and this will make her resentful. When EUF's dark side emerges, she can appear wounded – which will make her moany. If she finds a partner who will love and nurture her, she will blossom into a tantric priestess!

2. YOUR SEXUAL CHARACTER

Now you have identified your Sexual Personality Type, we are going to bring the typology model bang up to date by exploring your current personal desires and tastes. Although this set of questions may appear very light-hearted, we can identify quite a lot about our sexual character through our sensory preferences: what feels, smells, looks, sounds and tastes good to us. Our choice of what to wear, for example, may seem like a wholly conscious act, yet in each of us there is an unconscious code working away that predetermines our every decision. We become fluent at a deep level with society's signifiers and its currencies. Everything we surround ourselves with has associative values that announce what kind of person we are. It is an unspoken language that can say more to others than what actually comes out of our mouths. This is why appearance is so important to the persona we project. And, scarily, the sexual attract-iveness quotient within your appearance is measured by some on a scale of success or failure. A recent study for the *Times* newspaper revealed that 63 per cent of women bosses (as opposed to 53 per cent of male bosses) admit they automatically develop prejudices against a woman who doesn't wear make-up in the workplace. Does this mean that women have adopted male systems and made them even more rigorous, or have women been nurtured by a consumerist culture into being the more image- and body-conscious and body-critical of the genders? The answer is probably a bit of both. As we continue to adapt our working practices in the UK to an American model, the pressure to buff up and look stunning nine to five will become one of the requirements of employment. The good news is that we all have the power to make the best of ourselves, no matter what personality type we are.

This set of questions will get you thinking about the image you present to the world and what it is saying. There are no wrong or right answers. If you are not happy with your 'flavour', remember that personas can be changed and wallflowers can transform into spectacularly exotic blooms.

WHAT FLAVOUR IS YOUR SEXUALITY?

Q. 1 – What kind of clothes do you like to wear most often?

- (a) baggies that hide your lumps and bumps
- (b) normal, casual, whatever's clean
- (c) clothes that flatter your shape and maximise your sex appeal
- (d) you don't care as long as it has a designer label
- (e) fun and funky

Q. 2 – What kind of magazines do you prefer?

- (a) special interest/hobbies/puzzles
- (b) music/movies
- (c) fashion and style
- (d) current affairs/science/technology
- (e) celebrity chat and gossip

Q. 3 – What's your favourite kind of shop for browsing in?

(a) DIY

(b) music/bookshops

(c) big name department stores/cosmetics

(d) upmarket or designer clothing outlets

(e) twinkly/funky gift shops

Q. 4 – Which of the following men most appeals to you?

(a) Russell Crowe

(b) Orlando Bloom

(c) Laurence Llewelyn-Bowen

(d) Jeremy Paxman

(e) Jonny Wilkinson

Q. 5 – Which of the following fabrics do you like best next to your skin?

(a) soft/woollen

(b) crisp cotton

(c) satin/silk

(d) leather

(e) fur or feathers

Q. 6 – What kind of perfume most appeals to you?

(a) primal, musky

(b) fresh, lemony

(c) exotic, heady

(d) expensive, classic

(e) fruity, vibrant

Q. 7 – What colours do you prefer to wear?

  (a) black or dark blue

  (b) whatever's in season

  (c) exotic, warm (purple, terracotta, red)

  (d) classic/neutral: biscuit/cream

  (e) always a dash of colour

Q. 8 – When eating out, do you prefer:

  (a) Traditional English

  (b) Japanese

  (c) Italian

  (d) French

  (e) Indian/Thai/Indonesian

Q. 9 – What sort of holidays do you prefer?

  (a) camping in the countryside

  (b) activities: white water rafting, skiing, diving, etc.

  (c) city break with lots of cultural stuff

  (d) luxury spa

  (e) sun, sea, sand and sex on the (18–30s) beach

Q. 10 – What's your favourite cocktail?

  (a) Piña Colada

  (b) Margarita

  (c) classic, very dry martini

  (d) Champagne cocktail

  (e) Cosmopolitan

Q. 11 – Out of these cars, which one would you prefer?

(a) a reliable upmarket saloon with good heating

(b) an ex-army jeep with leopard–print seat covers

(c) a sleek old Bentley with a walnut dash

(d) a sleek Mercedes convertible with a great sound system

(e) a funky VW beetle in a wild colour

Q. 12 – You're having a dinner party. What's likely to be on the menu?

(a) three courses of traditional fare

(b) variety of dips and tapas, with a serve-yourself main course, nothing formal

(c) spicy home-made curry followed by exotic fruits

(d) grown-up expensive entrées, adventurous main course and impressive wines

(e) rustic-style pasta and salad

Q. 13 – You're planning a movie night in with your partner. What's your favourite bill?

(a) action-packed adventure/thriller

(b) spine-chilling horror movie

(c) escapist historical or fantasy

(d) intellectual subtitled Euro drama

(e) romantic comedy

Q. 14 – You're having a cultural day out, at an art exhibition. Would you rather see:

(a) French Impressionists

(b) the latest Damien Hirst or Turner prize entries

(c) the dreamy Pre-Raphaelites or symbolists

(d) great pieces of b&w photography/photojournalism

(e) twentieth-century modernists: Picasso, the Surrealists, etc.

Q. 15 – What do you like to listen to in the morning?

(a) nothing or bird song

(b) indie rock station

(c) classical music

(d) news and views

(e) pop tunes or dance music

Q. 16 – Which of these cities most appeals to you for a sexy weekend break?

(a) Rome

(b) Reykjavik

(c) Paris

(d) New York

(e) Birmingham

Q. 17 – Which non-domestic animal appeals to you most out of the following?

(a) dolphin

(b) wolf

(c) reptile or snake

(d) lion or big cat

(e) chimpanzee or orang-utan

Q. 18 – What underwear do you wear most often?

(a) practical M&S briefs

(b) Calvin Klein for women

(c) lace-trimmed matching bra and pants

(d) satin or silk French knickers

(e) thong or girly cotton panties with bows and polka dots

Q. 19 – Which of these pairs of words holds the most erotic appeal for you?

(a) loving and tender

(b) wild and daring

(c) secret and forbidden

(d) sophisticated and expensive

(e) hot and saucy

Q. 20 – What would you most like your partner to cover you in?

(a) a goose-down duvet

(b) chocolate

(c) fragrant oils

(d) diamonds

(e) whipped cream

Now find out your flavour!

Mostly (a) – Milk and Honey

You're not big on strong flavours, preferring neutral, low-key or sweet tastes in most things. No one would say you are the boldest babe on the block, as you often hide your feminine charms under a respectable façade. You are not interested in keeping up with fashion or having the latest, trendy accessories, but you have the inner strength of knowing what you like and sticking to it. You may be thought unadventurous, but your determination wins the day when others are being flaky. You are also quite old-fashioned when it comes to dating, preferring the man to do the chasing. In addition to this, you are not impressed by weedy men. You like clearly delineated roles for yourself and the man in your life and are happiest with a down-to-earth rugged type. You are a little apprehensive about allowing your sensual side to shine through, being embarrassed with the thought that you might be displaying a taste for anything raunchy, although you secretly enjoy a bit of raunch! Underneath your 'vanilla' persona is a woman who wants to be swept away and ravished. But after the passion is dealt with, there's nothing you like more than to snuggle up and be cosy in your little sanctuary, safe with your hunky man from the discordant rattling of fashionable urbanites. You will long for a country retreat and somewhere you can be close to nature. You love animals and are the type of person who will downshift from the rat race to keep chickens and make a comfortable nest for yourself and your family. But don't go too mad with that chintz!

The movie that best represents your flavour is *Emma*

The drink that best represents your flavour is **Bailey's**

The colour that best represents your flavour is **white**

The perfume that best represents your flavour is **Anais Anais**

Mostly (b) – Urban Zest

Your flavour is a delicate but exclusive one at the cutting edge of taste. You like luxury and do not run with the pack. You are big on design, were probably the first person in your street to get an iPod, and you present an image of casual cool. You are probably a Thinking type, and definitely groove on intelligent men and witty conversation. You like to be seduced by someone with a level of intellectual charm. You prefer an uncluttered environment and an uncluttered relationship. Underneath your relaxed, hip veneer, you are a woman of action and steely determination. You have a keen sense of quality and an unquenchable thirst for improvement – for yourself and for things around you. You cannot abide anything too homely or traditional, and your ideal living space is a bright, modern studio apartment. Your sexuality is defined by your sense of cool; you are languid and feline and come alive in a cosmopolitan environment. You cannot abide men who are desperate and drooling for your attention.

The movie that best represents your flavour is **anything by Pedro Almodovar**

The drink that best represents your flavour is **Bison Vodka**

The colour that best represents your flavour is **khaki**

The perfume that best represents your flavour is **Issey Miyake's Eau d'Issey**

Mostly (c) – Aromatic Spice

Darling, only the best will do for you! You love to cultivate an image of exoticism with just a hint of decadence. You don't announce your sexuality with bells and whistles, but you seduce through the latent hedonism that follows you around like a musky aroma. Men are intrigued by you as you do not go looking for their approval before you command an air of haughty respect.

You have a penchant for glamour and drama and theatrical set-dressing. You love the chance to be flamboyant and to dress up. You are a true sensualist who cannot resist stroking materials like velvet and satin. You like to adorn yourself and your surroundings with sensual fabrics and sparkling accessories. Hell for you would be a camping holiday, and you would rather be publicly whipped than caught in a Poundsaver shop. You would be at home in a stately mansion or landscaped gardens where you can flaunt yourself around the fountains being attended to by your minions. It's a shame that the aristocracy is dying out!

The movie that best represents your flavour is *Moulin Rouge*

The drink that best represents your flavour is a **spicy Armagnac**

The colour that best represents your flavour is **purple**

The perfume that best represents your flavour is **Opium**

Mostly (d) – Champagne Dream

This is the score of someone who has a taste for ultimate elegance and is the flavour profile that matches the IST type in the previous section. Your ideal scene for seduction is within the corridors of power or at a stylish hotel. You are an ambitious high-flyer with her eyes on the prize, someone that will always have a bottle of bubbly in the fridge just in case. You love cities, and can see yourself hailing a Manhattan cab to take you to Bloomingdale's for the afternoon for a little luxury retail therapy. You will not feel comfortable dating a man who is professionally not on the same level as yourself, as power and status is what turns you on! When it comes to your living space, you will aim for the best and dream of the even better. The sky is the limit as far as your aspirations go, and you adore exclusivity. When you do let go sexually, you are a tigress, and like to use your whole apartment for your lovemaking. You expect a man with stamina!

The movie that best represents your flavour is *Breakfast at Tiffany's*

The drink that best represents your flavour is **Bollinger**

The colour that best represents your flavour is **red**

The perfume that best represents your flavour is **Joy by Jean Patou**

Mostly (e) – Cherry Bomb

With this score, you are most likely to have rated as an extravert in the previous chapter. You are fun and funky and love having people around you and parties to go to. You are always up for a laugh and absolutely adore flirting in a cheeky way. You have a sunny, youthful exuberance that carries people along with you. Men can picture themselves running along a beach with you in the sunset. You like lots of colour around you and are the first one to go for a fashion craze. You revel in being a real girly girl – and it suits you. You like living with others, and probably share a house with a bunch of twenty-somethings. When it comes to the opposite sex, you like sporty men who can be romantic and heroic. You are an optimist and can get along well with just about everyone. You make the best of things and can even have a good time on a tight budget. You don't torture yourself by thinking about all the things that you can't have but make the best of what you do have.

The movie that best represents your flavour is *Austin Powers*

The drink that best represents your flavour is **rum punch**

The colour that best represents your flavour is **hot pink**

The perfume that best represents your flavour is **Jean-Paul Gaultier's signature fragrance**

HOW SEXUALLY CONFIDENT ARE YOU?

Whatever your sexuality, it is likely you will rate confidence pretty high up on your list of attractive personality traits. Sexual confidence is like a magnet; it will draw people to you, and not just potential lovers but new friends and professional contacts. Hiding one's charms under a blanket of modesty or nerves is more likely to put people off than attract them – others will pick up the signal that you have something to hide rather than that you are shy. Unlike in Jane Austen's era, these days we don't have the time to court each other with lengthy and impressive letter-writing and the occasional suggestive wave of a fan on a chaperoned walk. We have to display our confidence, but make sure we do it in ways that are not going to come over as too overbearing or desperate.

Sexual confidence is about more than being able to attract someone. It is also about being happy in our own company, and not thinking that we have to spend every moment of our free time with a partner because we aren't valid as a single unit. If we feel happy with ourselves and are able to enjoy the quiet times to explore our own interests rather than worry about our love life, we often find that we have more to offer our lovers when we are with them. We will glow with zest and vitality and attract people to us as if we were the proverbial ray of sunshine. It is important to spend quality time on pampering yourself at least one evening a week, replenishing your batteries and making sure you get enough rest so that you have the energy when you need it. On this note, having good sleep is one of the best things we can do to ensure sexual happiness. Our libido levels suffer if we regularly get less than seven hours sleep per night.

Q. 1 – What do you honestly think your friends would say most applies to you?

(a) you are a little wallflower who seems to get left behind when the party happens

(b) you are a little reserved but open up after a few drinks and conversations

(c) you are a confident flirt who comes alive in a crowd

(d) you give out the come-on signals to the point that they worry about you!

Q. 2 – You are facing a weekend left to your own devices. Does the prospect:

(a) sadden you

(b) not bother you

(c) please you

(d) appal you

Q. 3 – When you walk down the street, do you usually:

(a) look at the ground

(b) look straight ahead

(c) sneakily check everyone else out

(d) blatantly catch the eye of anyone who looks cute

Q. 4 – You have met someone new and it seems to be going well. Do you:

(a) tell no one as nothing may develop and then you'd look a fool

(b) drop it casually into conversation next time you see your friends

(c) act as if you've got a secret so you keep people guessing

(d) ring up all your mates and laugh about it

Q. 5 – Your opinion about a person's attractiveness differs wildly from that of your friends. Do you:

(a) keep your opinion to yourself

(b) agree with everyone else for an easy life

(c) voice it anyway and wait for the backlash

(d) revel in your difference

Q. 6 – You find yourself fantasising sexually about something odd or bizarre. Do you:

(a) worry that you're turning into a pervert

(b) try to change the course of your thoughts

(c) think there must be a logical reason and try to analyse it

(d) tell yourself what a wonderful thing the imagination is and enjoy it

Q. 7 – Someone unexpected or off limits makes a pass at you. Do you:

(a) tell him it's not a good idea and make a quick exit

(b) say you're flattered, but no thanks

(c) laugh and tell him not to be cheeky

(d) love the attention and go for it whatever the consequences

Q. 8 – Your date is not being as demonstrative as you had hoped. Do you:

(a) think there must be something about you that's off-putting

(b) make more effort yourself to provoke a reaction

(c) think that he's having an off day for whatever reason

(d) look at your watch, sigh, and tell him he has 'twenty seconds to comply'!

Q. 9 – Your partner loses his erection at a crucial moment. Do you:

(a) feel terrible. He must hate your body

(b) feel annoyed. He must have drunk too much booze

(c) not worry, and try again later

(d) get dressed and storm out in disgust

Q. 10 – You are offered a great job that means moving to another part of the country. The person you are dating has no desire to go. Do you:

(a) pass on the job and stay where you are

(b) make things work long-distance because you are determined to have both

- (c) make things work long-distance until you meet someone new
- (d) accept the job and part company

And when you are further along the line . . .

Q. 11 – You have been out together all evening and it's crunch time. Do you:
- (a) wrap your coat around yourself and wait for him to make the moves
- (b) make sure you are in close contact so he can grab you with ease for a goodnight kiss . . . or more
- (c) ask him what plans he has for you now, while striking a sexy but subtle pose
- (d) move his hand to your butt-cheeks and ask him to find your thong

Q. 12 – His kisses are a little wet. Do you:
- (a) put up with it and discreetly wipe your mouth
- (b) pull back subtly and hope he gets the hint
- (c) ask him if he has ever tried it 'this way'
- (d) ask him if he was a St Bernard in a former life

Q. 13 – You've had a lovely evening and now everything is in place for a night of seduction, except he seems a little nervous. Do you:
- (a) think he must have gone off you and don't pursue things
- (b) continue to show your interest through subtle body language

(c) actively up the sexy stakes with slow, seductive, hands-on contact

(d) take off your knickers and wrap them round his head, gusset inwards

Q. 14 – You find out your partner has a collection of adult mags or videos. How do you react?

(a) you worry that you don't look like a porn star

(b) you put it down to the predictable nature of the male sex drive

(c) you engineer it so that he catches *you* reading erotica one day

(d) you ask him to get them out so you can try some of the moves

Q. 15 – Your knickers are off for the first time in front of a new person. Do you:

(a) try to cover yourself with your hand or other piece of clothing

(b) look coy and make sure the lighting is low

(c) continue to flirt with him, using your now-exposed vagina as a tease tool

(d) grind yourself in his face

Q. 16 – Your new lover just cannot get the hang of how to stimulate you so you can orgasm. Do you:

(a) put up with it, hoping that it'll happen one day

(b) try to guide him with subtle hints

(c) find the right time to explain how you like it

(d) do it yourself after telling him to pay attention in case he might learn something

Q. 17 – You are about to climax for the first time with him. Do you:

(a) bite your hand and remain silent

(b) go into your own delicious moment but not make a big deal of it

(c) look him in the eyes and tell him you are about to come

(d) thrash around wildly and do a 'When Harry met Sally'

Q. 18 – Your partner has a knack for entering you in a way that is painful, but he seems to enjoy it. Do you:

(a) grit your teeth and bite the pillow

(b) whimper slightly and show that it hurts

(c) engage him in some other position before it happens again and explain why later

(d) howl and curse

Q. 19 – You have spent all afternoon in bed and now it's time to shower and get up. Do you:

(a) hide yourself in a long robe and slide out of bed so he can't spot your wobbly bits

(b) pull pants and a top or something silky around you and gracefully manoeuvre yourself to a standing position

(c) casually wrap a towel around your waist and saunter topless to the shower

(d) leap naked from the bed, not worrying about what you look like

Q. 20 – After having sex for the first time with a new lover, do you think:

(a) that's it, I'll be lucky to hear from him again

(b) oh well, another experience notched up

(c) he'll be feeling as good as you are and looking forward to the next time

(d) he'll be masturbating thinking about it

How Bright Is Your Sexual Confidence?

For every (a) answer, score 1 point; every (b) answer, score 2 points; every (c) answer, 3 points, and (d) answer, 4 points. Now add your total.

20–35

If you measured your sexual confidence in terms of light, you are currently generating at the level of a 40-watt bulb. Honey, you got to turn that voltage up a little or no one will be able to see what you have to offer. You may be in your late teens or early twenties, perhaps feeling a little unsure of yourself because you are lacking experience. Or you may have had a bad time with a lover and have taken a blow to your self-esteem. From here, if you want to play the game of desire and love, you can work towards being a little bolder. You are on the brink of all kinds of sexual discovery or re-discovery and need to dip your toe in the shark-infested waters. I know it's scary, but there are great rewards to be had by being more upfront about what you want. No man is going to castigate you for telling him – at the right moment – what you like done to you, and how soft or hard. If you are shy, then try to practise being coy rather than nervous. Check out my confidence tips at the end of this section and revisit yourself in a six months time. May the sexy force be with you!

36–50

You are caught in the headlights, unsure whether to leap into the action or retreat into the shadows. You have a businesslike or elegant air about you, but some people may find you a little stand-offish. You have a lot of potential for developing your sexual confidence – you just need to give yourself permission to let your hair down and you will soon uncover your wild side, rather than chickening out at the last minute. You like to be 100 per cent sure that you aren't going to make a fool of yourself sexually. But have you ever considered that your potential lover may be as nervous as you? You are a creature of subtlety and caution; although no one would label you a risk-taker, you are certainly able to spark men's interest in you through your reserve. You are like the sexy librarian who maintains a cool exterior but underneath . . . 'Why, Miss Jones, can you really do that with your mouth?!'

51–65

The sexual spotlight is on you! You display so much sexy confidence that you have the power to bring a man to an erotic fever pitch just thinking about what it would be like to bed you. You know that life is too short for putting up with mediocre sex, but you are so relaxed that if things do reach a sticking point in the bedroom, you actually enjoy teaching a man to get it right for you, picking your moment carefully so you don't hurt his feelings. Then you go on to share your pleasure with him. Maybe you are in your late 30s or early 40s – a woman's sexual peak – where she is happiest with her sexuality and no longer nervous of trying out stuff that a younger woman may be apprehensive of. You are a sexual sophisticate, fully tooled up with the attitude and the equipment for a mind-blowing time. You really enjoy radiating an erotic magnetism and, if you are at this stage now, will probably enjoy sex for the rest of your life.

66+

You are plugged into the National Grid, making such a show of yourself that you are blinding men to the real you. You are not just confident, you are an all-singing, all-dancing show-off who believes it is her right to demand sexual pleasure as and when she sees fit. Nothing wrong with that, but some people may think you tactless. If you can find a man who is of a similar type, I can guarantee that sparks will fly. It will be a tempestuous, passionate relationship as the both of you vie for the attention. You are either very young or very impatient – the sort of girl who would laugh at a small penis, not thinking of the consequences. No one would call you a sexual siren; more like a sexual foghorn! Go on and enjoy yourself, but try to consider other people's feelings occasionally or you will get the reputation as a man-eater.

MADDIE'S SEXUAL CONFIDENCE MASTERCLASS

Without sexual confidence, there can be no flirting. It is the springboard from which exciting things happen, and the bottom line for ensuring that your sexual relationships are successful. Being sexually confident doesn't mean that you swagger around boasting to your friends every time a guy looks at you. It's about keeping the part of you that is responsive to sensuality constantly primed and knowing the decisive moment to press it into service to your benefit. This is how you will be able to radiate the magnetism that will attract the people you want. Sexual confidence in action is like working magic, but how does one acquire it? I believe this is something that is built over a long period; it is difficult to snap from a lifetime of low self-esteem to super-charisma overnight. The more entrenched you are in negative thinking, the tougher it will be to reverse the process, but it is certainly possible, and many people have found new energy and joy in their lives by changing their lifestyle – doing simple things to increase a sense of well-being. If you are already a super-siren who turns heads when she walks into a room, you might skip this section, but I think there is something for everyone here. If you can't do them all, then try to do at least one that applies to the body, and one that applies to the mind. You never know, as well as increasing your sexual confidence, you may give your whole lifestyle a boost in the process!

1. Get out of your head

No, this doesn't mean what you think. This means diverting your attention away from your internal thoughts to other parts of your body and experiencing yourself as a total being. We live in our heads, especially as so many of us are in sedentary employment, becoming little more than a 'brain on a chair', constantly processing information and solving problems. It is a real boost to our well-being when we use our energy positively – for exercising our bodies – rather than negatively, when we are worrying about things. Of course, we all know that regular exercise is good for us, but my top tip for becoming more relaxed, more confident and more sensual is through the ancient health and healing discipline of yoga. For those of you who are put off by the idea of jumping around in a gym, this is the ideal way towards a total energy boost and body-improvement. In yoga, we are encouraged to focus on our breathing, posture, and overall well-being. It is also non-competitive, so we feel that it is designed for us uniquely. Almost all towns have yoga classes with courses catering for all levels. It is a testament to its power that yoga has stuck around. Basically, it works. It is not some flash-in-the-pan exercise fad that will look stupid in ten years time. You only need to practise once a week for a month to feel yourself becoming more in touch with your body. I guarantee that the endorphin rush you will get after a class will make you feel much more sensual and allow positive sexual energy to charge you from within. So, get out of your head and into your body!

2. Be enigmatic

Don't be shy, be fly! If you create an air of mystery about yourself, people will be curious and intrigued as to what your secret is − which, of course, is very sexy. Wearing your heart on your sleeve is not the way to go. You need to act as if you have the biggest secret and only the cleverest and most charming man can get it out of you. If we fancy someone, it is easy to make the mistake of looking too keen, hanging on their every word and being reactive to what they are doing, so bedazzled are we by their sexy persona. Next time you are in close proximity to your object of desire, try a 'less is more' approach − lure them to you rather than being caught in their headlights. We can fall into the trap of jabbering at someone when we fancy them, nervously chit-chatting about inane things just to fill the space between you.

Although it takes a little bit of courage, try to use your body language to good effect, giving off the signals that tell him you are a sensual woman without rattling on about your sister's wedding or the weather or other dull dialogue. Think of one or two cryptic or wickedly witty opening gambits and leave the fast chatter to him. As he ties himself in conversational knots, captivated by your mysterious sensuality, you can observe him thoroughly and languidly, taking in every detail of his luscious body. Believe me, it is worth engineering things so he does all the hard work, for the sexy rush of power you will get. The atmosphere will be electric!

3. Become a sexual idealist

Taking time to daydream about your ultimate sexual encounter is good for sexual self-confidence. If you have a number of internal practice runs at something you want to happen in real life, you are better equipped to deal with it when and if it does. No one can monitor what is going on inside your head. It is the ultimate freedom zone, so explore it and go as wild as you like. Don't repress those wishes! Try focusing on a person you fancy and running through potential sexual scenarios with them, imagining the dialogue or how you might answer them if they did make a pass at you. It is always good to be prepared. You can appear so much more confident and enigmatic if you can deliver a sassy line when it does happen than if you look at your feet, shuffle around and mumble a surprised 'OK'. Focus on getting what you want in your daydreams. Don't dwell on negative outcomes, but imagine that you win the day and drive him wild with lust. Imagine teasing this person, forcing him into making 100 per cent effort to get into your pants and relishing every moment of the delicious torment of delaying gratification. Realising the inevitability of a first-time encounter with a new person is the most liberating sensation we can experience sexually. It's a real Cheshire cat-grin, punch-the-air moment, and there are few things that beat it. Once you become aware of the potential fun two adults can have with each other, you can really tap into your in-built pleasure zones. Allow yourself the treat of letting your imagination work on your behalf.

4. Turn up your visual receptors

There is an old expression that goes, 'why can't a woman be more like a man?' This is certainly true when it comes to the visual sense. Men have spent centuries cultivating a culture where 'easy on the eye' images of women proliferate. What have we girls had to match the plethora of nudes, pin-ups, luscious paintings and posters of the sexually alluring female form? The answer is, not a lot. We have internalised our erotic sensibilities – this is why the vast majority of women prefer to read erotic fiction rather than look at visual sexual material. Men are relaxed about making their sexual preferences known – certainly in terms of aesthetics. OK, some of them are downright crude about it, but that raw honesty can be quite a turn-on in itself. Most women are not comfortable admitting that they can be aroused by looking or watching. As a gender, they are used to being looked *at*. We also attribute a rather negative opinion to those who become sexually stimulated through their visual sense – that it is somehow more 'base' and uncultured; the man in the raincoat idea of the sleazy voyeur – yet this is only a more basic form of what much highbrow art encapsulates under a more subtle veneer. When it comes down to it, biology and culture have always been closely entwined, so there is no need to feel guilty from looking at materials that arouse us. As women, we should try exploring what Freud called the 'scopophilic' drive – deriving pleasure through looking. In a practical sense, this is an extravert, externalised cognitive process. We look, we like, we lust – no problem. Finding pleasure through looking can take us away from the internalised process of constantly judging ourselves in relation to others. Next time you are confronted by sexualised images of (or real) men or women who evoke 'to-be-looked-at-ness' try appreciating them rationally from an aesthetic standpoint, rather than worrying how you compare with the idealised icon before you. You will find this an amazing relief! Forget all those dowdy arguments about objectification and just relax and enjoy yourself through your eyeballs for once!

5. Be yourself

Having the courage of our convictions and going for what we want as long as it harms no one, regardless of what others think, often pays dividends. Fortune favours the bold, as the old saying goes, and sexual fortune can certainly favour the more outspoken and innovative person who is prepared to go against the grain and be a maverick. It is always easy to tow the party line and be a follower but, when we look at the course of history, it is the bolshy and quirky individuals who find a place in our affection and who end up being national treasures, not the 'yes men' who play lapdog to the status quo. Power is an aphrodisiac, but so is rebellion with style. There is nothing sexier than the bad boy with talent or the smart girl with attitude. We all have strong opinions about something, yet it is the most introverted people who often feel the deepest passion. If you find you do not bring your passions from a common spring, as Edgar Allen Poe put it, revel in your difference and celebrate it, taking your audience with you. Cultivate your individuality and a quirky angle on the world, remembering that the conformists of life will fade into obscurity whereas you have something different to say. Be proud to be special and unusual and fly the freak flag!

6. Eat well

Eat well and prosper. Really, a bad diet will do nothing to increase sexual self-confidence. Feeling unattractive and sluggish means you won't get off first base in the flirting game as your self-esteem will be low and you won't feel worthy of attention. I'm not saying this applies to someone who is deemed by the dominant culture to be overweight or not conventionally attractive – not everyone has to look like a walking magazine photo. Plenty of larger or kooky-looking looking individuals can be super sexy and charming. This is not about adhering to prescribed standards of appearance. I'm talking about the effects of shovelling a daily diet of over-processed, high salt, high fat, low nutrient calories into your body and how that will make you feel. The proliferation of fast-food takeaways on our high streets has been disastrous for the health and well-being of the UK, building the idea that we live in a throwaway, undervalued culture. Many countries in the developing world have 'street food' that is far healthier and more nourishing than the lard-drenched options available to us in Britain, the US and Australia, where drive-through burger joints and deep-fried chicken huts are sometimes the only quick snacks we can access. It's not the high calories per se; it's what comprises them that can be the killer. This is a fact: a daily dose of saturated animal fats will make you feel awful, not least because of the chemical compounds squirted into factory farmed creatures when they are alive. Such food is rarely fresh and totally lacking in fibre – which is essential for a healthy bowel and digestive system. I'm not preaching vegetarianism from a perspective of killjoy Puritanism, but would urge you to consider choosing organic or free-range options if you do eat meat, and avoid fast food like the plague. The 'Five' rule – five portions of fruit and veg a day – is perfect for our general well-being, will increase our vitality and contribute to an all-round feeling of sexiness. We should eat a majority of foods that are still vibrant with life. It's a case of 'do the math': levels of obesity, heart disease, stomach and bowel cancers and depression have increased in the West at a level commensurate with the growth of fast-food outlets and processed food. How sexy is that? Er . . . not very. Stay fresh, organic and fruity and spurn the high-street fat machine as the devil incarnate!

7. Pamper yourself

Being in a strung-out state will make our spirit cloudy, and means we are not making the best of ourselves. No matter what your income or situation, you can do something to enhance or improve your well-being. We need regular rewards to feel cherished and worthwhile and, if we are not getting them from our lovers or family or workplace, we need to give them to ourselves. Pampering yourself shouldn't mean getting into huge debt so you can buy Prada handbags; it is the simple fact of treating yourself to small luxuries that you incorporate into your daily routine. One of the easiest ways to feel a bit special is to introduce some ritual into things like washing and cooking to remind ourselves that our life is sacred and that we deserve to be treated as nicely as possible. Pampering is really just another word for uplifting the spirit. While we are on esoteric matters, bear in mind that the yogic texts tell us we should never bring the day's residues into the bedroom, as it creates bad energy for lovemaking. Therefore we need to wash the office, the kitchen and the outdoor world from our bodies and psyches before we engage with lovers. No matter how basic your bathroom is, switch off the electric light, get some scented tea-lights around the bath and use a sensual foaming bath oil to trick your psyche into thinking you are in a holistic, natural spa – like a modern-day Cleopatra. Indulge yourself! Explore some of the aromatherapy products that are available. Natural oils and essences, such as neroli, sandalwood and patchouli are known to energise and uplift the spirit, so equip yourself with an oil burner and get into the practice of lighting candles in your living space. As much as possible, try to relax to music rather than television, or at least be a selective viewer as the TV saps energy from us and disturbs our psychic balance. If we feel we are looked after, we will give off a relaxed vibe and feel more deserving of sexual and sensual attention. Hence, better sexual confidence.

8. Improve your posture

It may seem a small thing, but bad posture can put people off wanting to get close to you. Hunched shoulders, a stooped back or a body language that gives out the message you would rather be nearer to the ground connotes victim status. If you give out the signal that you are downtrodden, people will perpetuate that cycle by ignoring you. A strong posture is sexy; it makes a person look as if they are ready to take on the world. Good posture comes from getting in touch with your core energy, and the best exercise for doing this is the relatively new fitness regime known as Pilates. Rather than just pulling back your shoulders, which can make you look like a regimental sergeant major, doing Pilates will improve your overall appearance, the way you walk and the way you carry yourself. It will even make you look taller. It works primarily on your stomach muscles, so that you become stronger from your centre outwards. I guarantee that after four weeks doing Pilates twice a week, someone will pay you the compliment that you are looking fantastic, fitter, slimmer or sexier.

9. Become your own sexpert

This book is a great start! But find out as much for yourself as you can about sex and relationships as opposed to leaving your love life to the chance hand of others. Masturbate, read sexy fiction, investigate the history of sexuality and sexual etiquette and get acquainted with the sexual pioneers. Also, investigate the greatest sexperts the world has ever seen: the Tantric practitioners of the Kama Sutra. The original Kama Sutra originated in India in the second century AD. Created in Sanskrit, the world's oldest form of writing, it is the earliest of numerous Hindu love manuals. The Kama Sutra says we should never accept 'mediocre sexual congress', and there is much we can learn from its philosophy, where sexual exploration is regarded as one of the most effective ways to achieve spiritual enlightenment. Western logic means that we have a long history of separating the body from the mind, thinking there is something dirty about sex. But this doesn't make sense in Tantric philosophy, in which the main principle is the idea of interconnected-ness – the link between ourselves and the universe we inhabit – body, mind *and* spirit. If esoteric Eastern philosophies aren't really your thing, there is always the French, who are credited with inventing sex- and erotic fiction. Seek out the writings of any of their literary greats and expose yourself to a whole new world of transgressive ideas. Even though the Marquis de Sade wasn't known for his healthy sex tips, you can always impress new lovers with your literary knowledge!

10. Increase your interest rate

Work on being someone who is interested rather than worry about being interes*ting*. People with sexual confidence don't walk around with a superior attitude or spend every spare moment bigging themselves up. They don't even spend much time talking about sex or looking obviously sexual. They attract others to them because people think they are inspiring and uplifting to talk to. The secret of being a great flirt is having the ability to get others to open up and talk about themselves. We always want more of people who are interested in us and ask our opinion on things. So, start asking people questions that will make them animated and enlivened. Good subjects include: What was your best trip abroad? What is your favourite song of all time? What's your favourite comedy show or what do you think is the best TV drama ever made? You will find that most people have a favourite in all these categories and this can be a great ice-breaker if your opinions differ significantly. Remember to listen to their answers – you don't want to make your conversation seem like an interview!

3. DATING AND RELATING

The image of the happy couple dominates advertising. There they are, drinking and dancing, texting each other, smooching in fancy restaurants, tumbling into beds covered in crisp white linen ... you know the score. Having a significant other is portrayed as being the natural but essential state of existence, and when you don't have a partner you can feel left out of the loop. How many of us have sat at a dinner party hoping the unattached friend of a friend who's been invited to make up the numbers will be someone you even want to talk to, let alone sleep with? There are so many permutations that need to be right, it is a wonder any couples get together at all! And once we have ticked the 'yes' box for attraction, availability, humour and politics, you then have to give off just the right amount of body language to let him know you are interested. This is where many relationships don't even get off the starting line. If you project the wrong vibes or fail to read the signals of seduction, the whole thing can go off the boil before you've even had a chance to get up close and personal. Unless one of you is confident and brave, it's a hit and miss circus.

Not everyone regularly attends dinner parties or has matchmaking friends. Most of us have to go it alone when looking for a lover. If you are really lucky you will be one of those 'factor X' girls who has never had to try too hard, has never known what it's like to be dumped, and only has to walk down the road to meet someone cute. However, the mortals among us have to rely on our social skills – flirting and conversation – or, if we're out on the town, dancing well and looking foxy. In 99 cases out of 100, you will meet a new lover when you are not trying, when you don't have that light flashing over your head that screams 'I'm desperate for a partner'. The best-known love-hungry person's secret is to never let your body language and vibes betray your long-term singleton status, even when you are going crazy to share your bed. Remember: there is nothing more off-putting to either sex than an overly keen wannabe lover, regardless of his or her looks – within reason, of course! Most of us like a cool or friendly approach, where we have time to metaphorically (or actually) dance around each other.

Remember that sexual tension is the biggest aphrodisiac – and is proven to increase the longevity of a partnership. It may take three months or three hours, depending on the circumstances and the people involved, but it is really worth building and stretching out for as long as you can, so the atmosphere reaches fever pitch. Remember: when a combustible chemical is compressed, the resulting explosion is always much more powerful! Of course, we are not always ideally placed to string out sexual tension for months. If you are travelling through Australia, for instance, and some surfer dude wants you to help him wax his board, you can't take a rain check for a week, but you still might care to arrange to meet him one hour later . . . keep him thinking about you. If you really fancy a guy who works in another department of your office block, however, you can stretch time a little longer. You might be biting your hand and going wild with your vibrator for a month or so, but it really is worth it. I'm not talking old-fashioned morals here – just empirical knowledge. Guys LOVE to work hard for their treats. It's one of those atavistic throwback syndromes where men feel that making an effort somehow reaps a better reward. This is probably something to do with hunting elk in distant prehistory, stalking prey for days until the moment was exactly right for attack. If you string him along for a while, he will feel that he's had to work extra hard for your affections, and he will get a glow of satisfaction thinking that, because you weren't too easy to trap, he must have bagged himself a choice catch. It also gives you time to work towards something better in the long run; gives you a chance to become friends – just good enough to still be able to pounce on each other, but not so good that you are round at his with the kettle on listening to his love-life problems. Once you are doing that, you will have gone off limits – consigned to 'girl pal' status.

Women seem to have an in-built finely tuned receiver that picks up the slightest signal of a man's erotic interest in them, or in one of their female friends. Men, however, are pretty hopeless in this area. Seventy-five per cent of them have poor antennae. You might think you're being as flirty as a cat in heat around a guy but you really have to make it obvious to him as he will not be programmed to identify subtleties in this way. Instead, men tend to be tuned to territorial threats. His awareness will pick up soon enough if he senses that another man is after his girl. As women are good at picking up the signals of seduction, so they also become expert at measuring sexual tension. You will know the 'decisive moment' in a flirtation when it is make or break time – and if he doesn't move in for the snog, then you will have to – before you end up being best mates.

However, in the first place you have to meet that 'someone' to create sexual tension with. The seduction process is like skilful angling. Like anyone looking for prime catch, you have the advantage if you've got good bait. But even if the bait itself isn't so juicy, it can always be dressed up with a little bright plumage. Then you have to throw out your line and hope that someone bites before you can reel him in, which is always the tricky part. OK, enough with the angling references. You know what I'm talking about: it is effort that is required. You are not going to attract a new lover by hiding yourself under a baggy jumper, keeping your head lowered, avoiding eye contact and shuffling around like you are ashamed of yourself. In order to meet people, you have to offer them something; show interest in them and interact. This goes for making friends as well as finding lovers. We all like to be spoken to by someone new; only the very rude or very busy won't respond to an obvious 'hello'. Think of the parties you have been to, and how great it makes you feel when a person you have never met before breaks the ice and asks you about yourself, seeming genuinely interested in you. It makes you feel part of something. Even if you are not used to playing the great seductress, go out with an air of confidence, and you will have a head start.

'But I don't have sexual confidence,' you may cry. Well, if this is the case, you may be lucky; you might meet someone who is prepared to bring you out of your shell and give you the reassurance you need. Many a person has sexually blossomed given respect and encouragement from a more confident lover. But, for the most part, the dating scene is pretty tough. Many people tell me how difficult it is to meet someone. These people all think they'll stand a better chance and gain that elusive confidence once they have acquired the qualities that society tells us makes us attractive: being slim, better off, in a smart new flat, in a new job, whatever. Many people, it seems, have their lives 'on hold', thinking they will be somehow 'better' when they get to a point where they are satisfied with themselves. Let me tell you, that point rarely arrives. It is futile playing the waiting game, thinking 'it'll be alright when . . .' Even if you get the job or the flat, there will always be another reason not to take the plunge. Believe me – the time is now.

The thing to do is to work on what you have in the here and now; make an honest assessment of how you relate to others, and look at the sexual signals you are giving out. The following questions are based on the original typology test, and the answers will help you to identify what you are doing right and where there is room for improvement in your modus operandi.

WHAT SEXUAL SIGNALS ARE YOU GIVING OUT?

Q. 1 – What kind of place do you like to try to meet a new lover?

(a) a crowded bar or club – somewhere with a party atmosphere

(b) a more upmarket bar with a more reserved clientele – a place where you can have seductive conversation

(c) the supermarket outside of peak shopping hours where you can flirt inappropriately by the carrots

(d) a coffee bar in a hip part of town where you can be cool and urban

(e) a gallery or library where you can be contemplative and intellectual

Q. 2 – Do you ever make eye contact with strangers?

(a) often

(b) only if they're cute

(c) only if they're cute *and* you're feeling adventurous

(d) rarely, you have to be drunk

(e) no way!

Q. 3 – You are stuck on a busy train. Are you more likely to:

(a) strike up a conversion with the nearest cute passenger to pass the time

(b) respond in a friendly way if someone else starts the talking

(c) flirt using eye contact and body language with the nearest fanciable guy

(d) bury your head deeper into your newspaper

(e) close your eyes and turn your Walkman up

Q. 4 – In social situations, which of the following most applies to you?

(a) you like a lot of personal space

(b) you don't mind people close by but you often unconsciously use 'defensive' tactics (holding a drink close to you/smoking/arms folded, etc.)

(c) you often lean on people or put your arms around them, touch them a lot in a 'Mediterranean' way

(d) you actively display a tactile, fluid sensuality

(e) you exuberantly show affection (kissing/groping, etc.)

Q. 5 – Do you usually keep your nails:

(a) neutral and short

(b) colourful and medium

(c) red and talon-like

   (d) full set acrylics with white tips

   (e) the above, with airbrush and stick-on jewels too

Q. 6 – You are at a party where your friends are otherwise occupied. Which person do you pick to chat to?

   (a) the coolest

   (b) the best-looking

   (c) the funniest

   (d) the wealthiest

   (e) the loneliest

Q. 7 – You've caught the eye of someone who interests you. Do you:

   (a) look away, embarrassed

   (b) smile sweetly and wait for him to approach you

   (c) smoulder at him, sit up straight and open a couple of shirt buttons

   (d) slowly move towards him, walking with your hips, maintaining eye contact

   (e) Wwve or shout over at him or make a direct bee-line

Q. 8 – OK, so you are introducing yourselves to each other. Do you:

   (a) let him talk about himself while you worry about what you are going to say

   (b) just go with the flow but respond to his lead

   (c) skilfully negotiate the conversation so that you are having a 50/50 interaction about the both of you

(d) don't talk about personal stuff at all but comment on general things and try to make him laugh

(e) give him your potted life history in five minutes

Q. 9 – You have moved somewhere where you can get a little more intimate. You are still interested in him. What's your body language?

(a) demure and slightly cautious; you don't want him to think you're easy

(b) relaxed but refined; you refrain from body contact

(c) seductive; you allow your hips, hands or legs to graze his

(d) cosy; you are acting like old friends already

(e) you already have your hand on his thigh

Q. 10 – It's time to part. Do you:

(a) wait for him to offer his phone number

(b) offer him your phone number and say 'call me'

(c) make the next date there and then

(d) book the taxi to take you both to the apartment of whichever of you lives nearest

(e) suggest a quick one round the back of the pub

Now count up your score

1. a = 5; b = 4; c = 3; d = 2; e = 1
2. a = 5; b = 4; c = 3; d = 2; e = 1
3. a = 5; b = 3; c = 4; d = 2; e = 1
4. a = 1; b = 2; c = 3; d = 4; e = 5
5. a = 1; b = 2; c = 4; d = 3; e = 5
6. a = 3; b = 4; c = 5; d = 1; e = 2

7. a=1; b=2; c=3; d=4; e=5
8. a=1; b=2; c=3; d=4; e=5
9. a=1; b=2; c=4; d=3; e=5
10. a=1; b=2; c=3; d=4; e=5

What signals are you giving out?

10–15

No entry! If you want to keep the wolves (and everyone else) from your door, you are going the right way about it. You are more likely to scowl than smile at strangers (probably because you are thinking too hard), and you put up quite a few barriers. Somewhere along the line, you lost your sexual confidence, but that doesn't mean you cannot change your ways. If you are happy repelling the delights along with the dangers, that's fine, but if you want to occasionally stick your head round the door and say 'Hello boys!' then you need to learn to interface more amenably with your fellow humans. Don't be shy. Nothing bad will happen if you try smiling for once. You never know, you could lure the man of your dreams.

16–21

Temporary parking. Does anyone know you're there? You are like a timid woodland creature that wants to drink at the pool with all the others but is too frightened that something will go wrong. Either this, or you are giving out such an air of urban cool that no one dare approach you. Your senses are finely tuned; you can pick out a likely lad from the crowd but, once you've spotted him, you're not sure what to do next. If you blush and lower your gaze, breaking eye contact with your potential new lover, he might think you're not interested.

Remember: faint heart never won the fit fella! You need to be bolder and prouder. Easily said, I know, but there are some tips for increasing sexual confidence at the end of this section. If you're the urban cool type, then you need to smile when someone looks at you so they know you're not really *that* scary.

22–30

Scenic route. Well, you are halfway to giving out the right signals, but you still feel more comfortable if the man makes the demonstrative moves. That's fine, but you could be missing out on someone really suitable who is as shy as you are of making their intentions known. Don't have a love life of 'if onlys'. If you follow your interest and trust your lustful intuition, you could have guys queuing up to take you out. Give yourself a sprinkling more sexual sparkle and confidence and you will be reeling him in. Maybe next time you go out, make a bigger effort with your clothes and body language and remember to vamp it up!

31–40

Dangerous curves ahead! You certainly seem to know what you want and how to get it. You are an expert at giving out sexy vibes without looking like you say yes to every guy you meet. You have no truck with false modesty – which is just as well, as most fellas don't understand that approach anyway – and have a sixth sense for what will drive a particular man wild. You have very well-tuned antennae for picking up interest signals, and you also know how to act upon them. You are something of a vamp, and appear to be doing very little in order to have a guy going crazy, hot and hard for you. The subtlety of your approach speaks volumes, and you have the upper hand over the more overt female predator, who can look cheap and tarty.

41–50

No stopping on the freeway! No one can accuse you of being backward in coming forward. When you spot a man you want, there is no mistaking your intentions, and you pull all the stops out to get him. The boys certainly get a green light all the way into your bed! You might like to try delaying gratification occasionally; perhaps cultivate a more subtle approach further down the line, but for now it's full steam ahead. Nothing wrong with that, but if you get tired of one-night-stands, or depressed that a guy doesn't seem to stick around long enough for breakfast, try the sexual tension tips at the end of this section.

TEN TIPS FOR MEETING PEOPLE

- Always go on the work outing/conference/workshop

- Attend an evening class that involves debate rather than physical exercise: philosophy/politics/psychology, etc. (i.e. nothing where you have to stick your legs in the air)

- Make an effort to talk to your friends' friends at parties

- Let your friends know the type of person you are looking for

- Get involved with something that interests you locally

- Find out what interest groups meet near to where you live (you'll be amazed by the variety)

- Go travelling

- Wear something colourful and funky (makes you seem approachable and fun)

- Offer to help people – you never know what it will lead to

- Walk, rather than take the car/tube/bus everywhere

TEN TIPS FOR GOOD FLIRTING

- Act as if you have the biggest juiciest secret and you're not going to let on what it is until he gets *really* close

- If you know his name, try teasing him with a gentle nickname or addressing him as Mr whoever (the sudden formality acts as an erotic jolt)

- Practise walking just that bit more sexily in front of him. Requires: heels, hips, an even pace

- Be opinionated – even if your opinions do not match his, you'll be able to debate, which is always good for building erotic tension

- Listen to what he says rather than worrying about what you look like

- Let your hair sway as you walk or, if it's short, run your fingers through it once or twice when talking to him

- Make sure you have mouth magic: lip gloss, fresh breath, sparkling teeth

- Great posture can work wonders for all shapes and sizes. It makes you appear confident – the greatest turn-on of all

- Cultivate being tactile: stroke things, toy with things, become more obviously sensual

- Don't be afraid to move in really close, but without touching

TEN TIPS FOR LOOKING EFFORTLESSLY SEXY

- Wear a bra that makes the best of your assets
- Make your nipples hard (a little toothpaste on them works wonders)
- Wear a zip-up top unzipped just enough
- Wear knee-high boots and a just-above-the-knee skirt
- Wear your hair as natural and shiny as possible
- Wear a tactile accessory: suede, creamy leather, feathers, satin
- Show off your curves with a fitted jacket
- Wear lip gloss over a neutral colour rather than a bright sticky warpaint mouth
- Expose your neck/part of your shoulder (not showing bra-strap, of course)
- Smile a lot!

BODY TALK

If we know how to read the signs, a person's body language can reveal what someone thinks about you. It is a really useful language to be fluent in – and can save you a lot of time and effort on the dating scene. The way a person carries himself in everyday life is a good indication of what he may be like in bed. If you have recently started seeing someone, pay attention to the way they interact with you and the world at large. Is their manner considerate, relaxed, aware, or is it stilted, gauche or nervous? Added to the overall picture are the details that can indicate whether or not a person is lying, what they really feel about something, or – the all-important one – if they fancy you. Over half the messages we receive about a person come through their body language. Around 35 per cent is from tone or intonation of a person's voice, with what is actually being said coming in at a measly seven per cent. Before you've even spoken to the person you fancy, the way you've walked into a room and carried yourself has accounted for more than 80 per cent of their first impression of you.

However, I would say that the genders differ slightly when it comes to making an assessment of a person's fanciability factor. Recent tests have shown that a woman decides whether or not she fancies a man within 90 seconds to four minutes of meeting him. I am sure that men make their assessment much quicker than this. Sight is the primary sense of the times we live in, and men, much more than women, rely on visual information for arousal. They are constantly checking out the shaggability rating of every woman that passes them, and make their decision based on how many signals fit in with what they find attractive: breasts, bottom, age, etc. The psychology of attraction is so complex, yet so immediate for males. The 50 billion dollar annual turnover for the porn industry bears out the fact that a man's eyes are hotwired to his penis.

So what about the girls? Well, women take a more holistic approach. Although a man's looks are important, women make an assessment of whether they will sleep with someone on a whole range of factors including posture, movement, intelligence and wit. Plenty of women groove on geeky guys who are a million miles from the square-jawed stud ubiquitous in magazine ads, so a man's attitude and brainpower can compensate for a lack of pecs. However, whereas a guy is not necessarily going to include a woman's social status into his fanciability criteria, women are real suckers for power. Being a company director seems to have the equivalent effect on a woman as a firm pair of 36DDs has on your average red-blooded man. A woman will overlook many of the down sides of a man, but a high ranking in the social or occupational hierarchy seems to be a winner. It's not only about the size of his wallet; it's that a successful man's body language will exude confidence – and women just adore sexual confidence.

BODY LANGUAGE SECRETS

These are the five rules that psychology experts have identified as body language giveaways. Give yourself the extra advantage next time you are on the prowl for a potential new lover by remembering the following advice.

1. Mirror action

One sure-fire thing that will tell you if a person is interested in you is if they mirror your movements. If you lean forward to impart something secret, they lean in to meet you. If you sit back, look them in the eye, and move your hand to your face, so will they. The reasoning behind copying another's actions is that we like people who are similar to ourselves. If someone is doing what we're doing, we feel they're on the same wavelength. If you want to try this out, don't copy someone's negative body language. If your target is huddling himself in a defensive manner, don't do the same, but try to steer his movements with your more positive ones. And don't do a 'Simon says'. As a general rule, wait around thirty seconds before mirroring a person's gestures.

2. Aiming true

We tend to angle ourselves directly at those we find attractive. Next time you are in the same room as the object of your desire, have a look at which way their feet, hands, legs are facing. Even if they are not looking into your eyes, or talking to you, you may find that they are unconsciously pointing their body at you. If this is the case, return the compliment.

3. Pupils and lashes

When we are talking to someone who interests us, our pupils dilate. This also happens at orgasm or when we have an endorphin rush through exercise or eating something pleasurable. It's a sign that we have relaxed because we are experiencing pleasure. Another sign of attraction is the old favourite of cartoon characters: the fluttering eyelashes, more commonly experienced as blinking. If you increase your blink rate, see if the person you are talking to copies your signal by increasing their own. Like the mirror action, they will unconsciously adjust their blink rate to keep pace with yours.

4. Raising an eyebrow

The most widely used form of friendly greeting across the world's cultures is a quick upward flash of the eyebrow. It is possible you may never have noticed it, but as it lasts only a fifth of a second, that is not surprising. Next time you cross paths with someone you fancy, watch for the eyebrow flash, or you can deliberately try lifting your own eyebrow for, say, one whole second, to give off that seemingly unconscious signal that you are interested in him. Watch and see if he returns the movement.

5. Zigzag

Different people elicit different facial behaviour, according to the level of intimacy appropriate to the situation. For instance, in a professional or business meeting, we perform a zigzag movement with our eyes, looking from eye to eye and avoiding the more 'personal' area of the mouth. With people who are our friends, our gaze relaxes and we allow our eye movement to roam a little – into a triangle that takes in the nose and the mouth. Once we are face-to-face with someone we fancy, the gaze drops even lower, to incorporate their whole body – hence the 'looking someone up and down' gesture that can be off-putting if it is too obvious. If someone you don't know particularly well looks at your mouth while you are talking to them, they might be wondering what it would be like to kiss you. Alternatively, they might be hard of hearing and are lip-reading, so don't jump to conclusions too soon! If the person you like displays two or more of these five gestures every time you meet them, this is a good indication that they fancy you. Happy flirting!

WHAT DOES YOUR DATE'S BODY LANGUAGE SAY TO YOU?

This is for those of you who have started seeing someone new and want to know what kind of lover your date is likely to be. In the early stages of going out, most couples are very attentive to each other. However, at some point in the dating game, we all find ourselves out with someone who would benefit from a session at a charm school. I have heard the most outrageous stories of men behaving appallingly on dates: 'forgetting' their wallets, showing obvious disinterest if the topic of conversation switches to something other than them, or groping the woman all night then leaving her to make her own way home after he has been fed and watered at her expense. On the other hand, you may find yourself out with someone who is so nervous he looks about to jump out of his skin if you even mention the word sex. If, after a couple of dates, you feel like it is hard work being with a person, don't carry on hoping that it will get better. You can usually trust your intuition on this one; you know when the chemistry feels right. Anything that feels like too much effort is best left alone – our lives are too short to spend time accommodating a loser or user. So, if you're not sure what your date's body language is saying, do this quiz and find out if he is a Nervous Nick or a Swaggering Stan.

Q. 1 – You hook up at an arranged meeting point. Does he:

(a) keep his hands in his pockets and smile

(b) gently put an arm around your shoulder

(c) kiss you on the cheek

(d) make a grab for your ass

Q. 2 – When you meet up with your date for a night on the town, he smells of:

(a) fear

(b) nothing or slight cologne

(c) strong aftershave

(d) booze and cigarettes

Q. 3 – You are seated in a bar with your date. You are talking about something that interests you. Does he:

(a) keep checking his mobile, watch, etc.

(b) seem relaxed and add to the conversation

(c) hang on your every word

(d) seem to be looking at your breasts but not listening to what you are saying

Q. 4 – You are at a party where you get separated from your date but you can see each other across the room. Does he:

(a) look up every few seconds to check you're OK

(b) smile

(c) call you over

(d) seem to forget you're there

Q. 5 – You are watching a movie together at home. Does your date:

(a) remain seated at one end of the sofa

(b) start at the end of the sofa, but gradually get closer

(c) get cosy with you immediately, legs, hands touching

(d) have his hand halfway up your skirt within five minutes

Q. 6 – You are about to leave or enter a building. Does your date:

(a) let you open the door and go first

(b) reach forward in a relaxed way to open the door for you

(c) leap ahead to open the door for you

(d) barge in front and not hold the door

Q. 7 – You are out at a party when you decide to dance to a slow song with your date. What's his body language?

(a) uncomfortable at the intimacy

(b) completely relaxed and happy

(c) holding you tightly to him so you are crushed

(d) lascivious, hands all over you

Q. 8 – You're out together when he runs into a friend. Does he:

(a) introduce you as a friend

(b) introduce you in a way that makes it known you are a bit special

(c) let you introduce yourself

(d) talk only to the friend as if you weren't there

Q. 9 – You are at the cinema and the movie you're watching features a sex scene. Does he:

(a) sink into his seat, embarrassed

(b) touch you in some way that communicates he'd like to be doing it with you

(c) keep looking at you for your reaction

(d) say: 'Phwoar, look at the tits on that.'

Q. 10 – You are in a shop or restaurant and someone assumes you are Mr and Mrs. Does he:

(a) cough and explain you are not

(b) laugh and play along

(c) say nothing but look decidedly uncomfortable

(d) say, 'You're joking, mate. I'm a confirmed bachelor!'

And if things have progressed a little further . . .

Q. 11 – The evening has progressed to the 'coffee back at mine' scenario. You are in the kitchen or living room at his place, does he seem:

(a) jittery, keeps leaving the room to check things

(b) totally at ease and welcoming

(c) fussy, asking you if everything is OK too often to be comfortable

(d) sexually impatient, with hands all over you

Q. 12 – You've finished the nightcap and it's crunch time. Does he:

(a) mumble that you are welcome to stay on the sofa or he will dial a cab for you

(b) tell you he'd love to spend the night with you, and will make breakfast in the morning

(c) beg you to stay

(d) lead you to his bedroom without fuss

Q. 13 – You have taken the plunge and entered his private quarters. What's on the floor?

(a) couple of newspapers, the occasional cup, books

(b) a sheepskin rug and scented candles

(c) nothing, it's spotless

(d) socks, underpants, porno mags and take-away cartons

Q. 14 – The music is on and he's making his move. Is it to:

- (a) sit down and tell you how wary he is of being hurt
- (b) compliment you on what great fun you have been that evening and say something cute
- (c) adjust his graphic equaliser
- (d) bite the top off the condom wrapper and tell you he's ready

Q. 15 – You are at the smooching stage. Are his kisses:

- (a) tender and loving
- (b) firing your erogenous zones
- (c) suffocating
- (d) dirty

Q. 16 – You have decided he fulfils your shaggability criteria and you are going to risk sharing his bed. Does he:

- (a) turn out the light and cuddle you first
- (b) make the room as comfortable as possible and start slowly loosening his/your clothes
- (c) immediately rip all his clothes off – except his socks
- (d) go immediately to 'fourth base', telling you it's your lucky night

Q. 17 – OK, so you are actually getting down to it. How much communication is going on?

- (a) he's constantly checking you're OK, that he's not hurting you, etc.
- (b) he's really enjoying himself but remembers to check you're having fun too

(c) he's not saying much, as he's concentrating really hard on the task in hand

(d) he just lets rip and satisfies himself

Q. 18 – What about your orgasm?

(a) he is really keen to please you but confesses he doesn't know where to start and goes off on a neurotic diatribe

(b) he has no fear of your clitoris and gets to it with variable-speed tongue and fingers

(c) he zones in for the right spot but doesn't look at all comfortable, making it hard for you to relax

(d) he wants to see you do it to yourself like an X-rated peep show

Q. 19 – How are things afterwards?

(a) he is cuddly and warm, if a little quiet

(b) he is warm and loving, and tells you that you are wonderful

(c) he is clingy as a koala

(d) he lies back, lights up and says, 'Blimey, girl, is that the time already?'

Q. 20 – The next morning, how does he act?

(a) he keeps apologising for anything that went 'wrong', the bed, the bathroom, what's in the fridge, etc.

(b) he wakes you up with breakfast in bed, as promised

(c) he wants to talk about when you will see each other again

(d) he dives straight in for a quickie before you're properly awake

Mostly (a)

Nervous Nick. This may mean that he's been hurt in the past, so go easy with him. But keep an eye on how he opens up to you. Perhaps you can make some movement to encourage him. Touch him fondly on the shoulder or occasionally brush his thigh when you are out together. Get closer to him physically and see how he responds. He should open up enough to return the same level of intimacy. If he is still really reserved after a couple of dates, he may need a lot of reassurance before he can relax enough to perform at a more sexual level. You will need to decide whether you think the reward of getting closer to him will justify the time you may have to spend coaxing him out of his shell. He may need lots of kissing and affection and could end up being a really sensitive lover. Some women prefer a guy who is happy to be led by them as he is unlikely to give it the macho swagger. Once you have gained his trust, he will make a loyal and loving partner.

Mostly (b)

Confident Carl. Here's a man who is happy in his own skin, has a few relationships under his belt and isn't bitter about past loves. He is generous, kind and attentive and his body language bodes well for closer contact. He is happy with you as an equal, not requiring your constant attention or approval, and is unlikely to be the sort to get jealous. If you are further down the line with him, and you have found that his confidence levels are as good in the bedroom as in social situations, then you will know that he has done his woman-pleasing homework and has probably read the latest findings about orgasm and female sexuality. He may even have books on the subject. The only drawback with guys this perfect is that they usually have a strong and well-defined ego that will need regular stimulation. His gaze may wander to other females even when you are with him. That is natural for men – remember what I said about their highly tuned visual sense. Sexually confident males like a regular diet of eye-candy. Watch out that he doesn't bore too easily, or you could end up running in circles around him to make sure he remains faithful. He will probably want a partner who always makes sure she's looking good – so no slobbing out, unless he is too.

Mostly (c)

Desperate Dan. Beware of the overly keen suitor. Finding yourself the total focus of a lover's attention to the point they watch your every move and hang on every word can be disconcerting and even uncomfortable. If you find his attentions a bit claustrophobic, you should drop hints early on that you like relaxed people and easy-going arrangements. Most men will get the picture. If he doesn't lighten up, disengage yourself from him. Getting shot of a clingy admirer can be a problem if you've already 'put out'. You need to lay ground rules with an ardent lover; don't compromise your plans to be with him alone if he starts demanding more of you than you want to give. Sometimes this kind of man can be lacking in confidence – you will need to work hard to bring him out of his shell. Plan activity dates where you can do things together rather than just sitting still watching movies or talking intimately in a bar. See how he behaves around your friends. Get their opinion of him. And see if he can laugh at himself; a man who takes himself too seriously all the time will be a tiring lover because we need to relax and have fun during sex, not tread on eggshells so we don't wound a fragile ego. If something goes wrong during sex, this type of lover may freak out and blow a small thing out of proportion. He may also take too long with the lovemaking – delaying his orgasm for ages to impress you, which, frankly, can be worse than sex being over too soon!

Mostly (d)

Swaggering Stan. This guy's a template for the archetypal arrogant sod. Has he ever been taught any manners or is he just so cocksure that he doesn't care what impression he is making? On the one hand he can be quite entertaining and even fun – for his bloke mates, that is – on the other he can be a real pain with a couple of lagers inside him. If you are prepared to put up with his sexist ways, and spar with him in a saucy manner, you may have a real laugh with Swaggering Stan. You may find that underneath his bravado is a more sensitive character than he is letting on. If he can drop his guard with you and learn to be loving – at least when you are together – he may be worth the emotional investment. He is the type most likely to buy you flowers and presents and treat you like a princess. But if after a few dates he turns out to be a boor in the bedroom, then get rid of this oaf before your friends start to drop you or he tries to get in their pants, too!

4. YOUR SEXUAL PSYCHE

The psyche is the deeper part of our selves – it is the mind *and* spirit, a mixture of the conscious and unconscious that is always seeking harmony and growth. The *sexual* psyche is a melting pot of influences that simmer and ferment inside us as we grow up, coming to the fore as we mature. It changes flavour throughout our lives as we are exposed to a variety of stimuli, but it finds its initial and most vibrant outlet during our teenage years, when our senses are awakened to this new, dynamic part of our selves. It is when we are most blatant about our likes and dislikes, when we form obsessive attachments to particular books or films, become politically active or vegetarian or desperate to impress. It is the time when we experiment with crazes, and when we develop erotic fixations on pop stars, teachers, actors and sports heroes – or even more curious crushes such as on a local bus driver or person in a shop who has a certain look.

Our sexualities are formed by a number of factors including genetic predisposition, family background, the ideas and imagery we are exposed to, and even the TV shows and advertising that are around at the time of our sexual awakening. Although we all share common experiences when growing up, we each develop a unique sexual framework through our individual interpretation of those experiences according to the Personality Type we have evolved. No one person has exactly the same set of experiences, and the multiplicity of variables means that each person's sexual psyche will differ from those of his or her peer group.

The family culture that surrounds us as we grow up plays a huge part in this process. The information we receive when we are young forms our attitudes to emotions and intimacy, and shapes our ideas of masculinity and femininity. Our caregivers have a huge responsibility in ensuring that our sex-role learning maintains an even keel. The sexual part of our selves is attached to the most primitive and sensitive regions of our minds and is easily bruised or distorted. If discussions about bodily functions or representations of sexuality were taboo in the household in which we grew up, it is likely that we may have formed some guilty feelings about sex and may find it difficult to share our intimate thoughts with others. Conversely, we may have rebelled against this censorship and have over-compensated for the repression by developing a wild or promiscuous side.

GROWING UP IN THE COMMERCIAL AGE

It is everyone's right to grow up in a loving family unit where we feel nurtured and our natural childhood curiosity is dealt with in ways that do not punish and scold. Our grandparents' generation and beyond had a notoriously difficult time explaining the 'facts of life' to their children, and many people grew up in ignorance of the basics of sex education. Prior to the Second World War, it was the norm that teenagers left school and were already working before they learned anything about sexual matters, and most did not have actual sex until married. But prior to the Second World War, sexual messages were not ingrained into commercial culture in the way they are now. Back then, advertising agencies did not know how to tap into our sexual psyches. If a company wanted to advertise its product, it merely showed us a picture of it and said it was good: 'Smoke Players', 'Drink Guinness', 'Eat Sausages', etc. There was no subtext of absent virility within the message; one didn't feel one was lacking until one was told. Ironically, it was the advances made in psychology and psychoanalysis in the second half of the twentieth century that contributed significantly to the mass explosion of media culture that we have today. An avalanche of sexual neuroses were being unearthed by doctors and analysts in the 1950s; decades of sexual repression were bursting to the surface as a result of war trauma, increasing mobility and the changing role of women. Generations of ignorance had definitely not led to bliss, but we would pay a new price for the advent of a more sexually open culture. Like the fable of the Emperor's new clothes, we suddenly realised we were naked; we needed something to cloak us and make us whole. Enter: the advertising industry, which stepped in to tell us about all the things we were missing. As soon as it realised how easy it was to tap into a nation's deep-rooted, long-tethered erotic desires, it became a whole lot easier to sell us stuff. The economy boomed as we realised, en masse, that we needed x, y and z to make us desirable, successful and cute. And as soon as teenagers became prime movers in the consumer game – with their new-found spending power and leisure time – the process went into overdrive. Advertising has had a huge influence on our collective sexual psyche, creating the erotic signifiers of the culture we have grown up in.

Our teenage years and early twenties are when we are most receptive to these influences. It is when we are impatient to adopt the accoutrements we think will speed our transition from the 'awkward' stage of late childhood toward adulthood and independence. And we are prepared to spend heavily to make it happen. Each generation of teenagers becomes a power-ful yet malleable force in the commercial arena – it is a fabulously re-active market, soaking up whatever it is told is cool. In this way teenagers are, for the most part, conservative – despite their predilection for music with parental advisory warnings. Underneath the most rebelli-ous adolescent there usually lurks a conformist: either a bad boy moulded to the prescribed values the music industry identifies as 'hard', or a glossy girlie who has ladled sugary babe-liciousness on herself from Barbie to J-Lo – with branded accessories available at the local shopping mall. A teenager who is actually something of an 'individual' (not interested in make-up or branded clothing, or who has an active interest in actually learning something), will get a hard time from the 'coolest' (read: most sexually advanced) of her peers, who will not be comfortable when faced with what they see as the immature or inverse version of themselves. This is extravert culture *in extremis*. Being genuinely different is largely off the agenda in the milieu of the sixth-form, and in society at large, as it is usually accompanied by an introverted persona – something not valued in a com-mercially dominant society that wants us buying in to the dream of sexual charisma as a purchasable commodity as soon as possible. Over the past decade, we have seen the sexual agenda rushed forward to include ever younger members of society. These days, even pre-teen girls and boys are aware of the importance of clothing, body image and which celebrities are the hottest – their parents' pockets siphoned of cash accordingly. This is OK up to a point, but when girls of 11 are dreaming of boob jobs, we have to wonder what changes are taking place in our collective sexual psychology.

One of the most exciting things we experience in our lives is the awakening of our sexuality. Yet it is certainly a time of emotional upheaval and distress, too, especially if we feel that we don't come up to the exacting standards of attractiveness as promoted by the ruling culture. The extra pressure of living in an increasingly consumerist society can make neurotics of us all. Young people need to develop strong inner selves, confident that they have much to offer the world, regardless of what labels they are wearing or what their bodies look like. They need strong role models and effective support networks to help them through this time of transition. Even though our society is heavily youth-oriented, the teenage years can be pretty miserable. Worrying statistics tell us that anorexia and other body-dysphasic conditions are on the rise in young teens at about the same levels as obesity. Young people are especially vulnerable to 'manufactured desire' and the current split personality that prevails around body image. With a raft of magazines dedicated to exposing the 'flaws' of celebrities, whom we build up to knock down, it's no wonder that many young women feel confused, some making themselves so miserable they literally want to 'disappear'. Ideally, they come through this horrible stage of self-doubt and self-loathing to realise there is not only one reality; that each individual has her unique contribution to make to the world, regardless of how she measures up to the supermodels and the super-rich.

Whether or not our teens are traumatic or wildly exciting, or both, they are not known as our formative years for nothing. It is a time of firsts: first love, first lust, first job, first vote – maybe even first time living away from home, if you are lucky enough to afford it. The experiences we have in our childhood and adolescence are essential in forming the personalities we will carry throughout our adult lives. This is the foundation of our sexual development and can tell us more about ourselves than we may think. Your own sexual psyche is a unique pot-pourri of feelings and influences. So cast you mind back and see how your adolescence helped to form who you are today. This quiz isn't like the others; you won't be adding up your (a) or (b) answers to find out what 'type' you are. Select from the answer option that you feel is most relevant, although you might like to keep a note of your own answer, should none of the four options in each category apply. This section is mainly for reflection. Ideally it will activate your sexual psyche and get you thinking about the people and events that were special to you when you were younger, as well as those that resonate with you now. Realise where there are links between the person you are today and the person you were then. Do you think you might have changed the dominant part of your Personality Type? Are you shocked at how much you have changed, or how little? Have you changed your tastes radically or do the same things turn you on now as then? As each person has their own special turn-ons, it is not possible to generalise answers, although there will be much more about archetypes and recurrent fantasy figures in Chapter 5.

HOW HAS YOUR SEXUAL PSYCHE EVOLVED?

Q. 1 – What was the attitude towards sexual matters in the household in which you grew up?

(a) It was completely taboo and you grew up thinking there was something 'dirty' about it

(b) your parent/s made a clumsy attempt at trying to answer your questions but sex was never discussed openly

(c) sex education was explained calmly and sensitively and sex was discussed in the context of a loving relationship between adults

(d) it was treated flippantly, even inappropriately

How do you feel about explicitly sexual matters now?

(a) you still feel uncomfortable talking about sexual stuff and guilty about your more explicit thoughts

(b) you have actively sought to find out all you can about human sexuality as you find it fascinating

(c) you can take it or leave it. You are not really sexually motivated

(d) talking about sex makes you amused and a little embarrassed, but you are intrigued by it

Q. 2 – When you were a young teenager, how did you like to dress?

(a) rough and ready, jeans and trainers

(b) grown-up, but as sophisticated as possible

(c) provocatively, like the older girls with strong sex appeal

(d) in whatever was the latest fashion

How do you like to dress now?

(a) you still like to be comfortable rather than sexy

(b) you aim to look professional and businesslike

(c) you love to wear high heels and sexy clothes, even to work

(d) you follow fashion avidly

Q. 3 – Who was your first turn-on?

- (a) pop star or TV hero
- (b) classmate or boy down the road
- (c) fictional character in a movie or book
- (d) a crush on a teacher

Who turns you on now?

- (a) someone from the world of music or film
- (b) a colleague or someone you can't have
- (c) an imagined, fantasy man whom you haven't met yet
- (d) your partner

Q. 4 – What was your first sexual experience with another person?

- (a) it was when you lost your virginity
- (b) snogging and fumbling about secretly in the park
- (c) with your boyfriend or girlfriend in your bedroom when your parents were out
- (d) looking at porn mags or websites with mates

What is sex like for you now?

- (a) always a bit nerve-wracking. You're never sure if you are doing it right
- (b) it's always a thrill, especially when it's with a new person. You get a real high from it
- (c) you enjoy it wholeheartedly and are usually the one to initiate things
- (d) you don't really have regular sex

Q. 5 – How did you feel around the opposite sex when you were in your early teens?

   (a) awkward and shy

   (b) excited and giggly

   (c) confident and show-offy

   (d) fine, at ease

How do you relate to men now?

   (a) you find the company of men intimidating as you are something of an introvert

   (b) you are shy but intrigued

   (c) you love to tease and flirt

   (d) you relate to men more as a friend than as a sexual woman

Q. 6 – Did boys think you were:

   (a) goody two-shoes

   (b) stuck-up or weird

   (c) a good laugh

   (e) easy

What do you honestly think men think of you now?

   (a) you are one of the good girls whom they would have to get to know really well before she began to talk about sex

   (b) that you are a bit frosty or scary

   (c) you're 'one of the boys'

   (d) that they wouldn't have to work too hard to get you into bed

Q. 7 – Did you think boys of your own age were:
  (a) gross
  (b) a mystery
  (c) better company than girls
  (d) hot!

These days, do you like men:
  (a) your own age
  (b) younger
  (c) older
  (d) either much younger or much older

Q. 8 – If your parents found out you were dating a boy, did they:
  (a) go mad and ground you
  (b) talk to you calmly about it
  (c) invite him round for tea
  (d) not care less

What is your relationship like now with your mother or father, as regards your love life?
  (a) they know everything about it
  (b) you always invite your partners to meet them and it's pretty relaxed, on the whole
  (c) you like to keep your family and love life separate
  (d) they interfere too much for your liking

Q. 9 – When you lost your virginity, did you think:
  (a) was that it? It was overrated
  (b) at last! It was fantastic

(c) yawn. That was boring

(d) great, now I know how to get my own way

Looking back to when you lost your virginity, do you feel you:

(a) should have waited until you were older

(b) wish you had had more knowledge and sex education

(c) think it was the start of a wonderful new world of fun

(d) should have made more of a celebration of it, like a rite of passage

Q. 10 – Looking back at your first sexual experiences, were they:

(a) practically non-existent

(b) disappointing

(c) wild fun

(d) probably unhealthy

Looking back at your sexual experiences since then, have they largely been:

(a) disappointing, men have not really come up to your expectations

(b) wild, roller-coaster times that are part of being young and crazy

(c) you still haven't really connected with the sexual part of yourself yet

(d) really enjoyable and part of your overall sense of well-being

OUR CHANGING PSYCHE

Remember that your sexual psyche changes over the years. Our late teens, twenties and early thirties is the extravert time of our life. Even if we are an introverted Personality Type, the matters we are concerned with during this period – i.e. gaining qualifications, building careers, perhaps buying our first home and having children and getting married – belong to the exterior part of life. Although our inner life – especially our fantasy life – is strong when we are young, we are more likely to cultivate a closer relationship with our psyches in the second part of our lives. After thirty-five, we tend to devote more thinking time towards the internal, philosophical questions. And by this time, we should feel comfortable with our sexuality; not so dominated by it, and freed up, in a sense, to perhaps explore a more spiritual path – not that sex cannot be spiritual, of course. By mid-life our sexual framework should be a familiar part of our psychology and something we have explored to a good degree. We will be able to recognise our 'old favourites' and be easily able to spot our preferred physical type and know what turns us on. These triggers are part of the fabric of our sexual blueprint. The physical things that attract you to a person may seem quite random, but subtle motifs act as signifiers to our psyche and trigger associative resonances with archetypes, which is what we will explore in the next chapter.

5. YOUR SEXUAL IMAGINATION

THE PERSONA AND THE PERSONAL UNCONSCIOUS

We are now going to probe a little deeper into the unconscious – beneath your basic Personality Type and nearer to the root of your sexual imagination. Remember that the word 'personality' derives from 'persona': the public face we show to others. We all use our persona to operate in the world at large, with all that involves, but we also have an active inner life, whether or not we pay much attention to it. The **personal unconscious** is unique to each of us, and we don't have to share it with others if we don't want to. The personal unconscious contains the private and uncontrollable images and thoughts that burst forth in our dreams and fantasies. This is a non-judgmental zone; a place of mystery where our inner selves roam freely. It is a place of light and dark, good and evil, beauty and ugliness, where nothing is censored. Conscious thoughts that are 'uncomfortable' are banished into it, and new ideas emerge from it. It is important to spend time exploring the ideas and images that come out of our unconscious minds. Inspiration and information sometimes leap out of it, as if from nowhere, and often contain coded messages that can be analysed and used to tell us more about ourselves – for instance, through dream interpretation.

As well as the **personal unconscious**, there is also a **collective unconscious**. This is the term Jung used to describe the recognisable wishes, desires, symbols and imagery of groups of people, and society at large. Such collectives can be as large as the entire human race, or can be filed into categories of nation, race, gender, culture, age, etc. And it is within the collective unconscious that we find the **archetype** – a concept Jung originally used to apply to religious characters that had no physical existence in the material world. There is something special about archetypes; they play a powerful role within the unconscious and act as metaphors for all manner of ideas and experiences. Some simple archetypes would be: the wise old man, the hero, the fool, the *femme fatale*, the trickster. Each archetype has its own accompanying narrative or fable that becomes accessible initially during childhood in the form of fairy stories, mythical tales or religious stories. The Bible, for instance, is full of archetypes. Archetypal stories speak to us individually, and act as educational tools, allowing us as children to develop a fantasy life – what Jung called 'introverted play' – the unfettered use of the imagination. Jung saw introverted play as important to a child's development as the extraverted play of the schoolyard. This is where we learn to form links between conscious and unconscious processes and inner and outer worlds, blending elements from the living circumstances of the individual with the archetypal narratives of the collective unconscious.

As we grow up, somewhere along the line of our sexual development, our unfettered imagination starts to eroticise particular characters; to charge them with sexual power in order to give ourselves pleasure. Our erotic imagination acts like a huge fishing net, bringing to the surface a haul of private riches that we metaphorically feast upon. Our sexual fantasies are more than just 'naughty daydreams'. I believe they perform a number of important mental functions, allowing us pleasure through creativity, imagined involvement through role-play and the temporary resolution of psychological blockages.

EXPLORING FANTASY ARCHETYPES

Over the years that I have been researching sexual fantasy and erotic literature, I have found that particular characters recur time and time again in both male and female sexual fantasies. Some examples for women include: doctor, policeman, footballer, pirate, fireman, dark stranger, company director, 'bad boy'. For men we have: French maid, naughty schoolgirl, nurse, girl next door, foxy librarian, policewoman, air hostess, etc. These are all sexual archetypes as they come with individual narratives and represent more than 'mere' sexual attractiveness. As well as having the visual attributes that provoke a sexual thrill, these archetypes also do things that turn us on, performing functions that explore the sexual potential of their character type – the things that don't usually happen in real life. For instance, if we have a thing about a motorbike courier in his leathers, instead of imagining him merely delivering a package, we elaborate and fetishise him to an extent that, when accompanied by masturbation, will excite us to the point of orgasm. We focus on those elements that give us a frisson in everyday life but exaggerate them to a point of voyeuristic indulgence. In this way, women are as likely as men to objectify their icons of desire while engaged in the process of self-pleasure.

Once we have brought forth the potent archetype and 'fetishised' him, we then posit ourselves within the narrative, taking either an active or passive sexual role alongside our preferred characters. In this way, we are like film directors within our heads, 'casting' ourselves in our own personal adult movie, deciding whether we play a minor or major role in the activity, directing the script and the action in the way that will best reach a resolution of conflict, i.e. orgasm.

Many of us also have a deep need to overcome the psychological blockages that hold us back in everyday life. This is the tertiary facet of sexual fantasy; where our sexual imagination can come to our rescue. We unconsciously create fantasies that allow us to turn feelings of helplessness into feelings of power. If we have a preference for doctors, for example (a popular female fantasy involves being examined by a good-looking but 'cold' medic, and often in front of a group of trainee doctors), this means that we like to surrender sexual responsibility to someone more 'capable' than ourselves. Someone with such a fantasy may at some level feel that she is not getting enough attention in real life, and may compensate by being the 'star of the show' in her sexual fantasies. In a survey conducted by Black Lace books, the exhibitionist or show-off fantasy was the most popular female fantasy. I would interpret this as meaning there are a lot of women out there who are not getting the attention they crave. And many of the women who confessed to this type of fantasy imagined themselves to be slimmer/younger/prettier than they said were in reality. In this way, the fantasist is fetishising herself according to society's preferred model of being; the fantasy of being fancied to the point that a man will lose control can be seen as compensating for low self-esteem in a person's real life, where they are not causing any such stir. If only for a few moments you can access the experience of being adored, then you are also able to access the emotional security that accompanies the feeling of self-worth, rather than self-loathing that is the inevitable result of being told you are not valid if you are not young/beautiful/slim, etc. This is fantasy working on our behalf at a deep psychological level to make us feel better about ourselves. Initially, a woman fantasising about being the favoured lap-dancer in a strip club may be thought to be self-obsessed or narcissistic when in reality she is the opposite.

Fantasy as compensation for low self-esteem works for both genders. A man who is under a lot of pressure to achieve in his working life may compensate for feelings of professional inadequacy by fantasising about non-threatening women, i.e. the 'girl next door', with whom he *can* feel powerful. In his imagination she is going to be happy with him whatever he does and will be grateful for his attention. The girl next door often comes with a narrative of naivety – being new to sex and unsophisticated so that the fantasist is easily able to impress her. She may not have seen a penis before, displaying an innocent enthusiasm for his equipment. She may take a submissive or inadvertently 'sluttish' role, being unfamiliar with sexual display like some *enfant sauvage* overtaken by her newly awakened instinct.

This theory of compensation is partly what Dr Michael Bader has identified as the 'portable first-aid kit for our psyches'. In his book *Arousal – The Secret Logic of Sexual Fantasies* – he explains how we tend to use fantasy characters as a means to experiencing pleasure safely and privately. Our unconscious mind seeks to solve – rather than add to – the problems we may encounter around self-esteem and sex by prompting us to fantasise about specific characters. An astute therapist will be able to have a good stab at what might constitute a client's sexual fantasies by listening to their worries about their perceived failings in everyday life.

It is useful to make mental notes about what arouses you as you progress though your life. Different stages of our lives will throw up different fantasy characters according to our ideas of self-worth, where and who we are within a social structure, or how we think we rate on a scale of attractiveness. Our sexual imagination can tell us more about ourselves than may at first be apparent. Have a look at the following questions and think about your own fantasies within the context of the compensation theory. You may find that the results reveal information that goes deeper than superficial notions of attractiveness; they may tell you something about your unconscious need to envision archetypal narratives. This section is longer than the other quizzes, and you get the answers as you go, rather than totalling scores at the end. This is where we get into the nuts and bolts of what triggers arousal, so the content is pretty hot. There are some real-life X-rated fantasies in section 6, taken from Black Lace readers' letters, along with their analysis. The more self-knowledge you have, the more sexual confidence you build up. So take the plunge and start to explore the most secret part of your sexual imagination!

WHAT ARE YOUR FAVOURITE ARCHETYPES?

Q.1 – What build of man most often populates your fantasies?

(a) rough diamond 'builder' – stocky

(b) fit adventurer – muscular/sporty

(c) everyday 'boy next door' – just normal

(d) stylish and fashion-conscious – slim and slinky

If you like (a) best, you get a thrill from being aware of the traditional differences between the sexes. You like your fantasy man to be a man, and enjoy imagining scenarios where such a man is attracted to you because of your body or what you are wearing. He is basic and simple in his needs, but determined to get his own way once he sees a woman he fancies. Your fantasies probably involve you being dressed really sexily for him, disarming him with a flash of your knickers or breasts. You like this type of man because he is easily aroused and will respond immediately to your visual display. He is the guy that crudely announces his lust when he sees a woman he fancies and is not apprehensive of showing his sexual appetite. Basically, you revel in being female and enjoy all the girly self-pampering that precedes seducing the rough diamond type. His build connotes capability and, to a certain extent, brutishness; you enjoy feeling physically vulnerable as a counterbalance to his strength. You want to be on the receiving end of a good seeing-to from a desirable man who will not take no for an answer. When you were younger, you most likely preferred the attention of your dad or older male relatives to that of the female members of the family, as it gave you a feeling of security and pride and opened your senses to the things that connote 'maleness' – the masculine smell, capability, authority, etc. If your fantasy man is of this physical type, then he is probably filling a need for physical or emotional security. Psychologically, you find security through physicality.

If you ticked (b) you have a strong awareness of the physical delineation between yourself and your man. You like to think about yourself being with a guy who does something noble or impressive with his body, and who looks after himself, eats well and doesn't allow himself to slob out. This build of man represents the archetypal 'hero' figure; someone resourceful, daring and brave.

Most likely your sexual fantasies involve an alpha male whose character matches his physical prowess – an achiever, professional type or authority figure who will take sexual responsibility. Whilst the 'rough diamond' type will not be able to control his desire for you, this type will be a master of it, driving you wild by being disciplined enough to resist you whilst maintaining a huge erection. This is the physical build most often found in the uniformed type that inhabits the majority of female fantasies. The pleasure of the fantasy comes through the act of him finally acknowledging his arousal. You may well be turned on by this type exacting some form of erotic punishment on you: spanking you or tying you up for teasing him and getting him hard. You like to take his mind off his noble, vocational activities, making yourself important to him through your ability to distract him. It is very likely that you dream of having more adventurous sex, compensating for the rather predictable nature of real sexual conquest with something far more sporting and playful. Psychologically, you find security through external authority.

If you prefer (c), then you are more likely to be aroused by physical sensation than those who chose (a) or (b). You don't go in much for sexual mind games or fantasies where your vulnerability (whether physical or psychological) is an issue. You fantasise primarily on the basis of the individual rather than on his obvious physical attributes and aren't much concerned with being anyone other than you. In your imagination you most often fantasise about sex with your real partner rather than a fantasy archetype. You have no need to work out any major issues through your sexual thoughts, preferring to concentrate on thinking about acts such as oral sex or sex in romantic natural settings.

You are the sort of person who likes to take life easy and not be constantly battling with the world. You are probably a sentimental girl at heart whose favourite way to spend a Saturday night is curled up on the sofa with your guy and a good movie. You are not much bothered by his pecs and abs, as long as he's kind and generous and has a good sense of humour. Psychologically, you find security through familiarity.

If you like (d) – the slim and slinky fashion-conscious type – you are very conscious of the sexual messages that operate through a person's clothes and appearance. You don't care if a guy can install a washing machine as much as wear a pair of low-slung pants and Dolce and Gabbana shirt with panache. You probably have celebrity fantasies, equating sexual attractiveness with the achievement of wealth. Maybe you dream of attending high-class orgies in luxurious surroundings where you can show off your assets and be admired by the beautiful people and attended to by servants. You have high standards and cannot tolerate being seen with anyone boring-looking or, God forbid, with a beer belly or bad haircut, which you see as a sign of weakness. You take pride in stepping out in style and like the attention that rewards your efforts. You are a sensualist at heart who wants to enjoy the finer things in life. At a deeper level, you use your fantasies to transcend the mundane reality of life. The slender male fashion model has something of the bisexual or androgynous about him, allowing you access to the unusual and exclusive. Psychologically, you find security through exclusivity.

Q. 2 – Which of these types would you most like half an hour of raunchy sex with?

(a) stripped-to-the-waist builder

(b) suit-wearing city slicker

(c) college professor or academic

(d) young horny skater boy

If you answered (a) you're the kind of girl who pretends to be annoyed when workmen call out to you in the street but you will use this later for your private fantasies. You love men to talk dirty to you but your arousal response is triggered by visual signals – usually the primary 'male' sexual sense. A tanned torso and bulging lunch box will get you going in the same way as a pert pair of breasts or long legs will turn a man on. You like it fast and furious, and like to get right down to penetrative sex without too much foreplay. You understand the animal side of passion, and are not afraid to 'get your hands dirty', as it were. You love a big hard penis, and relish giving it the treatment it deserves! You are probably very physical and active in the way you express yourself, and are not one to lie back and expect him to do all the work.

If you answered (b) you are the type who loves to tease and who knows the sexual power women hold over men. You get a real buzz when an executive type turns to look at you. He's supposed to be deep in concentration about his job and the money markets but you are so sexy that he just can't help himself when you're around. You are probably an exhibitionist, and you get a strong sexual thrill out of showing off your body. You like it when men do all the work and you can bask in the glory of being worshipped. Your fantasies are probably rather elaborate, always with you as the centre of attention. You know exactly what it takes to drive men wild and thrive off the satisfaction that comes with sexual conquest.

If you answered (c) then you understand that sometimes 'less is more'. You are not one for an explicit display, preferring a more subtle approach that works slowly but surely to strip away the layers of respectability to reveal the wild, animal man beneath. You love intellectual mind games, seducing through conversation where you know the object of your desire is as likely to be impressed by your brain as your physical attributes. You love sexual tension, and often go for men who are a challenge to your skills of seduction. You find intelligence a turn-on, and are intrigued by a man's sexual imagination. You may also have a darker side to your sexuality and may be intrigued by S&M or power games. You are likely to be sexually adventurous, and not thwarted by other people's moral codes. You love the idea of an illicit affair with a married man and the thought of passionate trysts in the afternoon. You want danger and excitement but within the confines of a mutually satisfying 'arrangement'.

If you prefer (d), then you are not much interested in sexual mind games but prefer to get down to business and not waste time. Like 'b', you are something of an exhibitionist and get a big thrill from the thought of being some horny guy's fantasy. You like the enthusiasm and energy of a young partner, and you see sex as a way to have fun and release tension. You don't like your sex partners to get too clingy, and like to think of yourself as something of a free spirit. You love the idea of 'flings' rather than relationships, and may be a little unconventional in your approach to life, seeking out alternative cultures. You've probably been backpacking to warm climates and are more impressed by someone's music collection than their career potential. You like people for who they are rather than what they own, and have a rebellious streak. You are an optimist with a strong social conscience. You like kissing and are hedonistic. Physical sensation is everything to you, especially when it comes from a fit young male body with an every-ready love tool!

Q. 3 – Which of the following occupation-fantasy figures do you find most arousing?

(a) fireman

(b) policeman

(c) doctor or dentist

(d) soldier

If you went for the fireman, then you are not alone. The fireman is the most popular British woman's fantasy archetype. When we fantasise about firemen, we don't think about the day-to-day job they do. And forget those jokes about hoses and helmets. He is the most popular fantasy archetype because he represents to us the perfect balance of ruggedness and bravery. And he wears a uniform – although he is not an authority figure like the policeman; this is not a fantasy archetype about control, even though the uniform is a fetish. Unlike other occupation fantasy types, fantasies about firemen often involve them being in groups, i.e. four or five of them rush into our bathroom, as we have locked ourselves in and need rescuing, all soapy and naked. The fireman fantasy is usually a very happy one and evokes the exhibitionist in the female psyche; we want to entertain him, strip for him, and give him a good time because he works so hard for our safety.

The policeman fantasy is complex and is rooted in the sexual aspects of control and power. Police fantasies mean being on the receiving end of the law, with all the paraphernalia that involves. It is often a fetishistic fantasy involving handcuffs, uniforms, restraint and punishment. We've been a bad girl and now we are going to be 'dealt with' in some way. Although on first sight this would appear to be the fantasy of a sexual submissive, what we are in fact doing is using our female sexuality to overthrow the power of an authority archetype. We are usurping his professionalism and righteousness through our feminine wiles. If he is engaged in a sexual encounter with us while on duty, then we have taken his mind off the job. And most likely he is going to be annoyed in some way about that. We might imagine that he is enjoying thinking that he is taking advantage of us, but it is really us who is manipulating him. It is the fantasy of someone who wants more control somewhere in their life.

The doctor has been a romantic fantasy archetype for decades, but the British penchant for naughty nurses and Carry On films has done much to transform him into a saucy fetish character. The medical fetish usually requires that the doctor or nurse be sporting his white coat. That's his uniform – what triggers our bad behaviour in the role of the patient. Unlike other occupations, this is one of the few where bodily examinations are expected. There can be few things more inappropriate than playing up during a medical examination – all that close contact, leaning across our bodies, the probing and inspecting. The medical fantasy is the fantasy of someone who wants permission to behave badly. We want to surrender responsibility to this fetishised, capable other who is, literally, clinical, i.e. not about to allow emotions to get in the way. The medical fantasy is often the fantasy of someone who wants an anonymous or inappropriate encounter. A doctor who is a trusted personal friend of mine told me that in the three years he has been practising as a GP, no less than 15 women have asked him for examinations in a way that left no doubt as to their intentions. This is an extraordinarily high number of people. One would expect that to happen perhaps over the course of a career, but three years! Of course, whether this fascinating statistic is related to the boredom of Home Counties living or is symptomatic of a national obsession I am unable to deduce. But it certainly shows that female patients can make sexual advances every bit as inappropriate as their male counterparts do to nurses.

The soldier is a trained killing machine. To fantasise about having sex with one is the nearest thing to a bestial fantasy without involving a real animal! From the polished guardsman to the muddy squaddie, we're talking seriously fit and ready for action. He's pumped up with muscle and testosterone and we want some of that heading for our bed. One gets the idea that he won't be overly concerned with romantic frippery; what we will get will be the raw man, the literal hard man who has to take his sexual pleasure where he can find it, as he never knows when he will called to the harsh world of battle. Many women find the thought of being on the receiving end of male sexual aggression wildly exciting. Although many women crave loving, emotional bonding during sex, the same number of women use sexual fantasy to concoct scenarios involving the very opposite. If we think about rough sex in the context of the compensation theory, we have to conclude that these fantasies involve the fantasist craving the total attention of another.

Q. 4 – What is the predominant quality of your fantasy man?

   (a) dirty-talking and down to earth

   (b) kinky or pervy

   (c) romantic or shy

   (d) wild and imaginative

(a) You love being a naughty girl. You may be quite shy initially but you love it when men display their arousal for you by telling you what they would like to do to you. As long as you know you are not going to be told off for acting 'slutty', you actually really enjoy it. You have no problem with men looking at adult magazines or being sexually demanding. You respond instantly to male attention and probably fantasise about being a lap dancer or being in the showers with a bunch of guys after a rugby match.

(b) You like drama and display. You want sex to be about more than physical sensation and you like the idea of transgressing convention and causing a bit of a stir. You relish the opportunity to dress up in kinky outfits as you like the effect this has on a man. You like to 'play' and see sex as a good way of getting in touch with your natural urge to perform and show off. You don't want to be one of the crowd, and like to cultivate a more exotic persona.

(c) You want to be a seductress and the one who is pushing things along. You like the idea of a shy man so you can introduce him to all the saucy delights of your sexual repertoire. You are aroused by the idea of the boy next door who is secretly bursting with desire and hard in his pants. Let's face it: no girl is going to get off thinking about hearts and flowers; that stuff is always about sex underneath. You like to use the acceptable idea of romance to fuel fantasies about taking control of a less experienced lover.

(d) You love the sense of freedom you get from orgasm. You want to be taken on a roller-coaster ride to excess. You are hedonistic and like to be introduced to new things. You want to notch up sexual firsts but need a lover to be more wild and crazy than you so you can justify your behaviour. You have an active fantasy life that involves all manner of accoutrements and environments.

Q. 5 – In your sexual fantasies, what role does the guy play?

    (a) sexually dominant
    (b) teasing or showing off
    (c) sexually submissive
    (d) no actual man features in your fantasies

(a) Most women prefer a sexually dominant lover in their fantasies. This doesn't mean they want to take a back seat in other areas of their lives; it's not about being subjugated in society. The reason that a sexually dominant man is such a potent archetype in fantasy is that he knows what you want without you having to ask for it. In fantasy, being caring and sensitive tends to work against the arousal factor. In real life, of course we want someone with these qualities, but in our fantasies, where we can let go and allow our minds to explore what we really like, it works better if he is something of a brute. From an early age we learn to 'suspend disbelief' when watching cartoons or hearing children's fantasy or fairy stories. We like to be thrilled by something scary and powerful that we know isn't really going to hurt us. This follows through to how we fantasise sexually when we are grown up. We can call up the dominant male and we can banish him at will. He is as much a familiar archetype as the big-breasted nympho blonde stereotype who 'does it' for men. Few people want to spend their lives with such characters, but they serve a useful purpose in getting us to orgasm.

(b) If you fantasise about men teasing you, showing off, stripping or masturbating, but not making obvious moves to overpower and penetrate you, your sexual motivation is actually quite 'masculine', as it is voyeuristic. Very few women have fantasies that involve voyeurism as this takes them out of the involvement. It means they are not getting attention, and we girls do like attention! To be voyeuristic means that you are fascinated by the forbidden, and get a sexual thrill from things that are naughty or 'feel wrong'. It is a tendency of the male sexual psyche to objectify what is sexually desirable, i.e. focusing on a woman slowly removing her panties. If you like, for instance, the image of a guy stroking himself through his boxer shorts or being involved in a delicious wanking session, you are objectifying him. And there is nothing wrong with that. You are merely getting pleasure out of what millions of men enjoy doing every day. If, on the other hand, you like to fantasise about showing off and teasing a man, you are getting off on being exhibitionist. Voyeurism and exhibitionism are two sides of the same coin. Both involve distance from a partner, and are less about emotions than sensation-seeking.

(c) It is slightly more unusual for a woman to fantasise about being physically sexually dominant and overpowering a man. Women usually prefer to over-power men psychologically. Most women who confess to enjoying rough play prefer in the end to be overpowered themselves and 'done to'. There are some recognisable dominatrix fantasies, though, where the subjugation of the male is paramount. The idea of having a man crawling around at your feet and worshipping you, or of being tied up and helpless is a total inversion of 'acceptable' sexual behaviour, and is in some way connected to a revenge fantasy. If you are lacking power in your everyday life it is quite logical that you might have fantasies of tying up your boss and torturing him! Some women like to fantasise about anally penetrating a man. This again sends a trigger that such behaviour is 'wrong', but it is the illicit charge that makes such a fantasy powerful.

(d) If a man doesn't feature in your fantasies at all, you are unusual in that you are driven to orgasm by physical sensation alone – unless you are having lesbian fantasies, of course (more about those later). It is very rare, although not unheard of, for a woman to masturbate concentrating only on the feeling and not thinking about anything else. This is a practice used in tantric sex, for building energy and tapping into other forms of con-sciousness. It could be that you have fantasies that are more disparate or unusual, such as thinking about non-human entities (aliens, vampires, etc.) or abstract concepts such as the feel of particular materials.

Q. 6 – How many of the following do you find sexually arousing? (Tick as many as apply.) Whilst some of these options may seem a little strong, they appeared regularly in the fantasies of hundreds of women, as surveyed by Black Lace books. Of course, none of these categories are about real-life incidents. We don't always fantasise about what we want to really happen. 'Dark' characters are no more real than the bad guy of fairy stories.

Submissive category

1. being chased
2. being tied up
3. being made to perform oral sex
4. being spanked
5. being forced to do humiliating things
6. being 'raped'
7. being gang banged
8. being masturbated over
9. being whipped or caned
10. being someone's 'slave'

Q. 7 – Same again. Give a tick to each element that appears in your fantasies.

Domination category

1. sexually teasing someone
2. making a lover call you 'mistress' or other formal term
3. making him beg for sex
4. tying him up
5. forcing him to wear what you want
6. forcing him to have sex with you
7. spanking or whipping him
8. pouring hot wax on him
9. making him your own personal slave
10. anally penetrating him

Q. 8 – And again . . .

Voyeuristic category

1. watching a guy shower
2. spying on a guy masturbating
3. paying a guy to strip for you
4. secretly watching a couple having sex
5. watching two guys together
6. observing men watching women lap dance for them
7. using binoculars to spy on someone through their window
8. watching a couple having sex with their knowledge
9. making a dirty phone call
10. performing sexual/psychological experiments on someone

Q. 9 – And again . . .

Exhibitionist category

1. flashing someone from a moving vehicle
2. stripping for your partner
3. masturbating for your boyfriend
4. letting your boyfriend watch you pee
5. wearing an overtly sexual outfit for your boyfriend
6. flashing someone where they can catch you
7. stripping for a group of strangers
8. masturbating for a group of strangers
9. letting a stranger watch you pee
10. wearing an overtly sexual outfit in the company of strangers

Add up how many you ticked in each category – one point for each 1–5 answer; 2 points for every 6–10 answer.

Submission

0–5

You have thought about sexual submission but you don't feel comfortable thinking about yourself on the receiving end of another's sexual aggression, even though it is imaginary. Your fantasies may involve some element of pursuit, but you draw the line when it gets too rough. You aren't sure that it is healthy to have such fantasies, and are confused as to why some women find them so appealing.

6–10

You are certainly intrigued by the idea of being at the mercy of a dominant archetype. You fully understand the difference between fantasy sexual aggression and the real thing. You crave sexual excitement and enjoy films and books that explore the dark side of human imagination. You love the idea of driving men wild and turning them on to a level where they cannot stand any more teasing and have to have you.

11–15

There is no doubt about it: you are a full-on sexual submissive, excited by erotic subjugation and the thought of causing sexual mayhem in the aroused male. As much as the fantasy of being 'forced' into sex is about your 'submission' it is also an objectification of the dominant male archetype. In your fantasies he is reduced to having little more intelligence or consciousness than that of a grunting beast. We have to ask: who is the one being subjugated when the pleasure is all yours?

Domination

0–5

Well, you are unlikely to become the next Miss Whiplash. You are really not enamoured by having to make so much effort as that required by a convincing dom. You like the man to be the one in control. You are content with the power you derive from arousing him by your body alone; you don't need to get whips and boots out. To be honest, you find a grovelling man more of a turn-off than a turn-on.

6–10

Well, you get a certain frisson from having a man at your beck and call, and you love the warm, pampered feeling you get from having a human pet fawning after you. You probably have a good sense of theatricality, and can role-play well, although this is definitely a light-hearted, fun thing for you rather than a huge sexual thrill. You are not afraid to experiment, though.

11–15

Make way for the warrior princess! A man will be lucky to survive a night with you and leave with his dignity and his flesh in one piece! You really relish the thrill that comes from wielding sexual power. You see women as infinitely superior to men, and take every opportunity to ensure that your partner knows who's boss. You adore having an extensive wardrobe of tough, black, leathery or shiny clothes that galvanise you against the world and have him quivering like a jelly in fear and awe of your majesty. You are a rare creature – a happy dominant female who is prepared to take responsibility for her submissive partner's pleasure.

Exhibitionism

0–5

Eek! The thought of someone spotting you in a vulnerable state horrifies you. You like to expose your sexual self only to your trusted partner. You can't imagine how a woman could bare her all as a lap dancer or stripper. Even though you may be perfectly happy with your body, you are not about to give out the message that you are available. You have no intention of being the masturbatory fantasy of anyone!

6–10

You are quite excited by the thought of being fancied en masse by a group of men. You may not have ever actually flashed in public, but you love the *idea* of causing a scene – and like to fantasise over what effect you would have. You are a natural tease and a great flirt and you understand how much men like the idea of getting a look at something they are not supposed to. With every small thing you do that excites a man, you gradually become bolder.

11–15

If you haven't been arrested it's probably only a matter of time! You probably found early on in your life that showing off provokes a reaction and gets you attention. You were something of a wild child, no doubt, and now you are grown up you are a wild woman and a definite extravert. Other women feel wary around you, with good reason. You know exactly what to do to have a man hard in seconds. You are most likely out of all the categories to have acted out their fantasies. Your ideal scenario is to be shipped in somewhere and made to perform in front of a crowd of horny guys. Your partner will have a hard time (literally) keeping you under control!

Voyeurism

0–5

'Why would you want to invade another person's privacy?' you think. You are more likely to look away than get the binoculars out if you happen to catch someone unawares. You get no thrills from seeing a person undressing or doing something intimate. You are only likely to be interested in another's state of undress or self-pleasure if it is done with the full knowledge of your presence, and that person is your partner. Also, where's the fun if you aren't the object of attention?

6–10

You are intrigued by the idea of catching someone in a state of private contemplation. Oh, let's not be coy: the idea of watching a hunk playing with himself or a good-looking couple having sex does turn you on. You are at ease with the idea of lusting over a stranger or deriving pleasure from spying on another person without their consent as fuel for your fantasies. You get a thrill from the sense of 'getting away with it', and find it all a bit of a giggle.

11–15

You are a secret spy, obsessed with the idea of having access to something you shouldn't. This is an unusual emphasis in the female catalogue of fantasies as most women like to be somewhere in the frame as an object of attention. The voyeuristic fantasy is an introvert's fantasy, as it means not having to bother with engaging with real people. You need to find power somewhere in your life, and the thought of being able to observe others' private behaviour gives you a sense of guilty pleasure. You are the type who will adopt an assumed identity if you have the chance, but you need to believe more in yourself and realise that it is OK to discuss your sexual feelings. You may be missing out on interactive human experience.

Q. 10 – Have you got a wild side?

Women are far more elaborate and theatrical in their sexual fantasies than men. Whilst we like our heroes to be fit, a great body is not the only factor that does it for us; we also like a lot of set dressing. Whereas men focus on female anatomy for stimulation, women eroticise situations and environments as part of the overall fantasy. A woman is more likely to go off on wild flights of fancy, incorporating all kinds of elements that boost the power of the scenario. Clothes, textures and places play a huge part. The following questions do not have answers – they have one-word explanations that encapsulate the qualities of that element. After picking one in all four categories, you should have a combination of adjectives that make up your wild side.

Which male historical costume do you think is sexiest?

(a) Caveman – primal
(b) Roman gladiator – brutal
(c) pirate or highwayman – thrilling
(d) knight in shining armour – brave
(e) Regency dandy – poetic

(f) Victorian gentleman – disciplined

(g) the cad – louche

Which female fantasy outfit most appeals to you?

(a) warrior princess/fur bikini-clad cavewoman – wild

(b) highwaywoman – outlawed

(c) rustic milk maid – earthy

(d) Cleopatra – dangerous

(e) Vampire – devouring

(f) Moulin Rouge – exotic

(g) 70s groovy chick – funky

What would you most like to feel on your skin as you had sex?

(a) rubber – kinky

(b) mud – dirty

(c) oil – slippery

(d) leather – tough

(e) whipped cream – messy

(f) tarmac – hardcore

(g) crisp cotton – safe

Where would you most like to have sex?

(a) under a waterfall in a tropical lagoon – beautiful

(b) in an underground car park – sleazy

(c) in a luxury hotel room – spoilt

(d) on a football or rugby pitch in front of 5,000 fans – heroic

(e) at 35,000 ft in first class – exclusive

(f) in front of a roaring fire in a castle – romantic

(g) in a haunted house – scary

6. EXPLORING SEXUAL NARRATIVES

We've looked at the function played by archetypes in our sexual imagination but there is more to female sexual fantasy than just the characters involved. There is also the narrative – what we do with them. The following options are taken from the seven most popular female fantasies as voted by Black Lace readers.

Which is your favourite fantasy narrative out of the following?

1. sex with a colleague
2. lesbian sex
3. group sex
4. sex with a stranger
5. dressing up and showing off
6. sex with a celebrity
7. erotic punishment

SEVEN SAMPLE FANTASIES AND WHAT THEY MEAN

1. Sex with a colleague

'Lance had been working in our office about three weeks before I started to fantasise about him. He wasn't spectacularly good-looking or anything, but the way he started to look at me when the weather suddenly got much hotter and I began to wear summery tops that showed a fair bit of flesh made me feel all funny. If it had been anyone else I might have not liked the attention, but Lance was our senior line manager and very polite and proper, so it was fun to imagine him being consumed by lust. I used to have to go into his office with weekly reports and I know that he was thinking about having sex with me – you can just tell, can't you? He used to lean back from his desk when I went in and look me up and down, and I'm sure that I saw him with an erection once. I desperately wanted to put my hand on his thigh in one of our really boring management meetings, but never found the courage, as you can be sacked for that sort of thing. Instead I began to masturbate while thinking about him asking me to work late one night and coming up behind me when I had a short skirt on, running his hands all over my knickers, ripping them off and doing it to me over his desk. In my fantasies he goes crazy at being able to have sex with the company's hot young assistant (he's about forty-five and I'm twenty-four) and he comes really hard. It becomes our little secret and no one even guesses that anything is going on.'

Explanation

Thinking about sex with a colleague is inevitable. We spend more time with our colleagues than with our families. If you have a colleague attractive enough to provoke sexual reverie, then you are lucky! Many people work in jobs that are populated by a majority of same-gender employees, so finding a fanciable workmate can be a source of immense fun. This fantasy is about transcending the dull and the everyday, using the idea of sex as an escape from the world of work. How boring it is to be consumed only by the workplace rigours of productivity and balancing the accounts. Our unruly unconscious will always throw up images that transgress what we are 'supposed' to be concerned with. It is the anarchist within us, willing us to create chaos through forbidden pleasure. The work colleague is often the sexual archetype that will crop up in our dreams. In this example the sexual reverie is not so much a first-aid kit for the psyche as a trickster energy reminding us that we have the option to behave badly. However, I recommend that unless you both have a very good idea that you can keep such a liaison under wraps that you don't start having sex with a colleague – particularly if he works in the same office!

2. Lesbian sex

'My fantasy involves a woman who I often spot shopping in our small town. One day I'm in a café, when she comes in. There is nowhere for her to sit, so I invite her to sit with me. We get on really well and exchange telephone numbers. That evening she phones me and says she would like to show me some of the make-up that she sells in a large department store. I suspect that she is making excuses in order to see me again, so I arrange for her to come around while my husband is at work.

'It's summertime and very hot. She turns up wearing skimpy shorts and a tight-fitting T-shirt that sits very snugly over her ample firm breasts. I make her a cold drink while she goes outside in the garden to sit by the pool. I take out her drink and, as I pass it to her, I trip and the cold drink spills all over that tight T-shirt. Her nipples go rock hard instantly. There's a towel on the washing line, so I grab it and start drying her, which is just an excuse to touch her. I apologise profusely but she's not having any of it. She pulls me playfully into the sprinkler and soon I am wetter than she is. We both enjoy the sight of each other's breasts covered in the damp clingy fabric. Very soon the play turns hot and we start wrestling with each other on the lawn, rolling around in wet skimpy clothes. I love the feel of her womanly body pressed close to mine. The neighbours have come out to hear what all the commotion is, so we run inside giggling like a couple of teenagers. We go upstairs and she removes her top and bra, as do I. I can't help myself. I start caressing her nipples and kissing her. When I think about going any further than this, I come.'

Explanation

Most women will at some point wonder what it is like to have sex with another woman. This fantasy – and 'straight' women's lesbian fantasies in general – are about reclaiming the sense of naughtiness and the joy of discovery we had when we were teenagers. Many same-sex fantasies have a playful element. The association is usually one of freedom, unbound by the heterosexual sub-text of power games. The straight woman's lesbian fantasy will usually be about a very feminine woman – someone well-dressed or well-made-up who works in a lingerie store, for a cosmetics company or who has a very pronounced femininity. We all know how arousing men find the idea of two women together. Many women, too, get turned on by the idea of performing with another woman to give their boyfriend a thrill. In terms of archetypes, the lesbian is a beguiling mixture of masculine and feminine – and when it gets mixed up so that the very feminine-looking woman behaves in a butch way, or the leather dyke acts coy and girly, we are into some interesting territory. Or maybe this fantasy is about being able to have totally safe sex with a gorgeous creature who smells nice and looks great in silky underwear!

3. Group sex

'My favourite fantasy of the moment is set in a health club with my boyfriend. We are in the jacuzzi relaxing. I'm wearing a very low-cut swimsuit that reveals my slippery breasts. We start to feel very naughty, knowing we're all alone. My boyfriend's hand slips beneath the bubbling water and quickly finds its way to my sensitive spot. I slip my fingers around his penis, which is already standing to attention. He encourages me to position myself so that one of the water jets is aimed right between my legs. It feels wonderfully naughty, and soon I am in ecstasy. I haven't noticed that a guy has walked into the room, guessed what I am doing, and got hard inside his swimming trunks. My boyfriend has motioned for him to join us. As I orgasm from the force of the water jet, I open my eyes to see a very aroused stranger is kneeling at the side of the tub and, with encourage-ment from my boyfriend, I slip him into my mouth. After a few minutes we lay some towels down on the floor and I climb on top of my boyfriend, slipping him inside me slowly. I continue to suck on the guy's cock as I'm riding my guy. I feel delicious, with cocks filling me everywhere. I can't help myself from coming again. At the same time, I feel my boyfriend shoot his load. The guy in my mouth serves me a hot smooth portion and I eagerly take it all, loving every second!'

Explanation

The threesome, or its wilder sister, the orgy, is about being able to let go and allow your private side to be shared with more than one person – which takes a lot of guts and is synonymous with the breaking down of inhibitions – something most of us are keen to do. The idea of a tangle of limbs and lips and genitals all devoted

THE BLACK LACE SEXY QUIZ BOOK

to seeking pleasure evokes the image of Roman decadence or crazy parties one imagines goes on in stately homes. There is something truly hedonistic about having sex with more than one person at a time, although group sex features in the Kama Sutra for the purposes of raising energy levels, so it can't be that wrong, can it? Group sex definitely goes against most moral codes of religion and civilised behaviour; it is a sign of profligacy and unrestrained lust – all the more sinful because it needs group consent. The idea of a group of people dedicating no small amount of time to indulgences of the flesh has to make one think that privilege is at work. It was always the aristocracy who had the time and the power to indulge their fancy for three-way or multiple sex sessions in the eighteenth century, the time of the libertines. Most group sex fantasies actually involve the fantasist, their partner and one other person, rather than the heaving love-in image that defined the concept of orgies in the hippy era. In fact, many couples have introduced an acquaintance into their lovemaking and found a lot of pleasure from it. It is a fantasy one can realise relatively easily, although the emotional risks are obvious. One has to feel pretty secure in one's relationship to put such a naughty plan into action. The above fantasy involves two men – the reality being that most men don't feel comfortable sharing their partner with another man. However, the 'two girls and a fella' scenario usually scores highest in male fantasy.

4. Sex with a stranger

'I get on the 18.45 at Liverpool Street and it's packed, as usual. I'm feeling really wound up and have had a stressful day at work. Suddenly I become aware of the handsome guy standing next to me. We are so crushed that I can feel his hot breath making the hairs on the back of my neck stand on end. The thought of him getting hard starts to really arouse me, and when the train thins out a little I turn to look at him. He really does have an erection! We find seats opposite each other, and I am conscious of opening my legs a little, and pulling down my top so he can get a glimpse of cleavage, driving him wild. When my stop arrives I subtly motion for him to follow me, but I don't for a moment think he really will. Then I am walking up the pathway that is the exit from my station when I hear footsteps approaching behind me. He tells me that it isn't his stop but he has to know what I'm playing at. I take all my courage and invite him back to my flat. It feels really scary and thrilling when he walks into my flat with one thing on his mind. There is no point pretending, playing at offering him coffee or making small talk. He tells me that he wants to have me, there and then, and he does, over the coffee table. He doesn't even take his clothes off, and I am given the shag of a lifetime, able to let go as he pounds into me like a man starved of sex. When it is finished he thanks me, smiles and walks out. We don't even find out each other's names.'

Explanation

Sex without formal introduction flies in the face of 'civilised' behaviour. Acting on raw, primal instinct with no thought to the consequences is what animals do. Sometimes, for all of the closeness that a long-term relationship provides, many of us find it easier to completely let go and have wild uninhibited sex with those we don't know – and who don't know us. Obviously, such a practice runs a high risk of danger; one would need to pick one's stranger liaison extremely carefully. This said, there is an undeniably powerful thrill from the thought of instant mutual attraction to such a degree that you cannot pass up the opportunity to do what comes naturally. Isn't it just infuriating that we can attend a hundred parties where nothing happens but be in the supermarket when we spot that one person who gives us a jolt of fiery lust? Giving in to instant sexual desire is something we should all do at least once in our lives.

5. Dressing up and showing off

'My husband is involved in Sunday league football and it really turned me on when he told me that some of the lads have said how fit I am. I have started to fantasise about what it would be like to give them all a thrill, and show them just how fit their team-mate's missus actually is. I imagine that I go to meet him at the local club on a Sunday afternoon after they have played their game. I decide to give them all a private show in the back room, where I am the centre of attention. The beer is flowing, the music is on and there is a very male atmosphere. There's a stage at one end of the room, and rows of chairs are laid out in front of it. Gradually each chair is filled with Gary's team and their friends. The music is turned up and I walk on to the stage, wearing a short black skirt, hold-ups, knee-length boots and a tight black crop-top which makes my breasts look even bigger. Gary's face is an absolute picture as I start to move erotically around the stage, rubbing my hands over my breasts. My nipples stand hard and erect. I look into his eyes with such confidence as I slowly step off the stage and walk towards him. The other lads are cheering and calling out at me. I sit astride him and kiss him passionately. I can feel him hardening already. I stand up and walk around all the other lads, rubbing my body against some, kissing others and pushing my breasts into their faces. As I walk back to the stage, I start to take my top off to reveal my juicy firm breasts. Then I undo my skirt, pulling it down over my arse, slowly and seductively. Once it's off, all I have left on is my thong and hold-ups.

'I continue to dance slowly around the stage in my own little world. I am rubbing my hands over my breasts and in between my legs. Gary and his mates have stunned faces and I can see their erections forming in their trousers. I walk forward and kneel in front of Gary. I rub my hands up the insides of his thighs until they meet at his crotch. I look up at him with a grin on my face as I start to undo his jeans. I feel so powerful. Everyone is in suspense, wondering what I'm going to do next. I pull down his jeans to reveal his hard cock ready and waiting. I take it gently in my hands and slowly rub it up and down. I then lean forward and take him deep in my mouth. A groan of pleasure passes his lips as I take him deeper and deeper.

'I look around the room and notice that some of the lads have started masturbating. This gives me the courage to carry on, knowing that what I am doing is really turning them on. I then stand up and sit on top of his cock. It fills me deeply and I feel my body heating up as my orgasm approaches. I ride him slowly, grinding myself into him. I look deep into his eyes and he smiles with satisfaction and pride that his wife is so hot. I start to fuck him faster and he moans in ecstasy, as he frees my breasts and sucks on my erect nipples. Our lovemaking becomes extremely intense as we both reach the verge of our orgasms. With one final thrust, we both shout out in pleasure, and I feel his liquid flow into mine. The other lads are all sitting there with their cocks in their hands, coming all over the place. With a final kiss for my husband, I get off him and pick up my clothes and walk back on to the stage and out of the back door.'

Explanation

There is no doubt that this is the fantasy of someone who loves male attention. The show-off fantasy is the most common of female sexual reveries. Despite the huge gains made by feminism to improve women's status in society, the female ego continues to thrive on the kind of attention that can be 'earned' only from soliciting male approval. A woman can achieve the position of director or commander-in-chief of an organisation, but this will not satisfy her need for sexual admiration – the approval craved at some level by us all, but especially by women. The sexual show-off fantasy is the female power fantasy par excellence. There's nothing as arousing for a woman as knowing that the man she fancies is in her thrall. When a group of men is involved, then even better, as a whole room full of horny men lusting after you must prove you are desirable. The above fantasy feeds into this woman's ideal of herself as a sexual creature, yet one who can only dream of such a scenario. In reality, such a thing is highly unlikely; most men would not want their wife paraded as a sex object for other men, and the other men's partners would hate a woman taking the attention away from them. Fantasies like the above are a way of finding freedom for our imagination, creating ego-boosting scenarios where being provocative and luridly erotic is rewarded rather than punished.

6. Sex with a celebrity

'I have a real thing about the actor Russell Crowe. I nearly died when I saw him in the film *Master and Commander*. He could command me anytime and I'd do anything! He's so masculine and rugged and I go weak when I think about him. I even liked his character in *LA Confidential*, when he was fighting with Guy Pearce and when he was trying to seduce Kim Basinger. I like it that he's a bit of a bad boy and that he doesn't take any nonsense. That's probably partly because he is Australian. Anyway, I like to think that I am a reporter who is interviewing him at an awards ceremony. I get into his dressing room and he is furious but, instead of having me thrown out, he locks the door and tells me he is going to teach me a lesson. There are no preliminaries or pretensions towards seduction. It is rough and brutal as he rips my knickers off and talks dirty to me, telling me that he's going to shove it inside me and come. I am so predictable. Instead of fighting back I just melt as he does exactly what he has just threatened to. Afterwards, he realises how pretty I am and he sneaks me out the back door into his private car. He drives me to a luxury hotel, checks us in and we go crazy all weekend, doing it everywhere until we are both exhausted, by which time he has fallen in love with me.'

Explanation

Even though this fantasy involves rough sex, the celebrity fantasy is at its heart the stuff of romance. Women have been having these kinds of fantasies since feudal times, when the lord of the manor would descend on his villagers to practise *droit de seigneur* on the young maidens. It is about being validated by an admired other; the fact that an 'untouchable' icon has taken the time to bother with little old you. The idea of a celebrity taking us to bed is the equivalent of winning the lottery . . . it could be you, but the odds are stacked some 4 million to one against the chances of it happening. Without meaning to sound patronising, this fantasy is just a little bit juvenile as it means the imagination is not engaging with sexual scenarios that are even in the realms of possibility. Not that I have anything against Russell Crowe in a captain's uniform you must understand, far from it, but because many celebrity fantasies are about putting another human being on an impossibly high pedestal where we are so much lower down than them. And as we know, self-worth is the key to a happy sexual life.

7. Erotic punishment

'Male domination and being spanked is my sexual fantasy, although I've never allowed men to dominate me in everyday life. I love the thought of people in authority taking advantage of me, but only sexually! I love men in uniform, especially policemen. After a work-out at the gym, I feel I could rip the clothes off the first police officer I bump into.

'This is the fantasy I think about when I'm out walking during the summer months. I always feel very aroused when I walk about in the sun. No one is around, so I take my T-shirt off. I can feel the breeze on my body. It feels so good that I decide to let the air get to my breasts. I pull the front of my bra down so they are still supported but fully exposed. I start to play with them as I walk. I lick my fingers and gently rub the wet over my nipples. I feel the wetness between my legs and look around to check that nobody is about as I am so horny that I want to touch myself. I lay my T-shirt on the ground, sit down and pull my shorts down so I can relieve the throbbing between my legs. While I am squeezing my tits, I am also stimulating my clitoris. What I don't realise is that I am being watched. Once I have cried out my orgasm I open my eyes to see this man (he is always about fifty years old) standing over me, looking really angry. He tells me how I should be ashamed of myself. I say that I don't, so he says that he is going to teach me a lesson I won't forget. He grabs hold of my wrist and pulls me to my feet, takes me to a tree stump that is lying just behind us, sits down, puts me across his knee, pulls down my shorts and starts to give me a good spanking.

'My arse is on fire, and he slides his hand between my legs to feel how turned on I am by what he is doing. He tells me how bad I am and that I need to feel his belt. He bends me over the tree with my bare bottom exposed and hot. He slowly removes his belt and, after about six lashes across my cheeks, he drops his trousers and rams me hard from behind. I still don't know who he is, and never find out.'

Explanation

Erotic punishment storylines account for some eighty per cent of all erotic fiction novels. Being caught doing something naughty by someone in authority whom we have sexually aroused with our shameless behaviour is one of the most potent turn-ons in the whole gamut of fantasies. This is adult play at its most thrilling, involving chase, capture and, inevitably, a sore bottom. Most of us like to be 'done to' by someone who knows what they are doing, who can keep us in check with a firm hand that we know will bestow a loving caress as considerately as a sound spanking. Most women who are excited by this kind of fantasy will usually conjure up the image of an older man; someone perhaps of military bearing or in uniform. This will lend him the necessary authority that can't be acquired while wearing a jeans and jumper and will emphasise her vulnerability. This is the ultimate 'naughty girl's' fantasy – the loaded power dynamic where she pushes her infuriating minx-like behaviour to the level where a 'decent' man will lose control. When we are small, we push boundaries every day in order to learn our limits. It is part of our exploration of the world. As we get older, our horizons narrow somewhat, and the number of new things we do each day decreases. These fantasies may be so popular because they redress the balance of familiarity and introduce some simple and gleeful excitement that may be lacking in our day-to-day lives. Also, the combination of mock-anger and sexual arousal makes for a highly charged erotic atmosphere. The theatricality of role-play scenarios in real life can introduce a level of sophistication into a relationship, as you learn to relate to each other's assumed personas.

7. GETTING DOWN TO IT

Some of us seize the opportunities life throws at us with little caution as to the consequences. Others procrastinate, weighing up the pros and cons until the moment has passed and they can safely ruminate on the 'what ifs'. This applies to all aspects of life, but the decision whether or not to leap in with both feet applies particularly pertinently to sexual opportunities. When we risk 'asking someone out', we risk rejection – the cringe-making experience that makes us feel just that bit lower to the ground, or, depending on the circumstances, like one of the creepy crawly things. The longer we take to mentally run through possibilities, the more disastrous the imaginary scenarios we build up. Sometimes the only way to tackle it is to seize the day with gritted teeth and an optimistic air, with not much thought as to the outcome. If you've been following the tips in the sexual confidence masterclass, this shouldn't prove so daunting. The problems arise when a previously self-conscious person suddenly gets a rush of bravado borne out of desperation or too much drink and over-compensates for their shyness by behaving wackily – or lecherously – at the office party. Aside from this, and other tragi-comic scenarios, sexual opportunism is about having your antennae tuned to other people's interest. One thing that has always fascinated me is that we can pick up on unseen messages. We just *know* when someone is looking at us, even when our back is turned. Or we know when 'something is wrong'. It's another of those throwbacks to when we were cave-dwellers, when sight was not our primary sense, yet no one can explain *how* this works. If we tune our erotic receptors to the psyches of others, we can pick up the general indicators that silently give us permission to move the flirting to a higher level. For instance, two people can be having a perfectly polite, anodyne conversation about how the weather was on their respective holidays, yet a subtext will be occurring at a deeper psychological level that is speaking of how they would like to shag each other senseless. It is this sexy subtext that produces the wonderful frisson of erotic tension. Ideally, we all experience it more than once in our lives – the slightly faster heartbeat, the increased sensitivity of the skin, the dilating of the pupils and sudden thirst. Although these and other physical manifestations of desire feel like a highly personal response – something you have created from your own attraction to the person – I believe it is as much an experience of their interest for you as it is your reaction to them. There is much that we pick up at a subconscious level that we aren't taught to recognise. Body language is only scratching the surface. There is much communication that goes on that we cannot account for through the five senses alone that remains nameless and yet is very real. If you scored in the first chapter as an Intuitive type, you will have a head start here. If you are a Thinking type, you will probably rely on weighing up the rational probabilities that someone fancies you. A Sensation type will be the one most likely to miss out, as they will be waiting for an obvious signal, such as a hand on a thigh, before they get the green light. The Feeling type may wait too long to respond, even when another person is giving out obvious signals, as they will be worrying about the consequences and all the permutations of how they might feel, should they give in to their desires.

Whatever Personality Type you are, try practise tuning your psychic antennae to the erotic messages other people are giving out. Thinking and Sensation types, just trust your intuition; it is there! Note how your body reacts when different people stand near to you. Is there a specific type of person who causes a physical change in you, or one person in particular who makes you go all silly inside? Next time you feel that mysterious, exciting something, try giving them a sign that you are interested. They might move closer, then you respond, and then, and then . . . fast forward and you could be having the orgasms of your life! But until you have mastered the subtleties of the invisible language of attraction, how does your persona explore the erotic possibilities that come your way? Find out in this next quiz.

HOW SEXUALLY OPPORTUNISTIC ARE YOU?

Q. 1 – The insurance man/builder/plumber calls round to measure up your walls, sink, etc. and he's cute. Do you:

- (a) shake his hand and keep conversation to the professional details
- (b) make him tea and start a more general conversation
- (c) undress him with your eyes but in a subtle, sophisticated way
- (d) lick your lips and ask him if he usually wears his trousers that tight

Q. 2 – What do you honestly think your friends would say most applies to you?

- (a) you are extremely fussy about your choice of men
- (b) you are a little reserved but open up if someone makes an effort to flirt with you

(c) you are a flirt who will give anyone half decent a chance

(d) you give out the come-on signals to the point that they worry about you

Q. 3 – What animal best describes your personality?

(a) pussy cat

(b) dog

(c) tigress

(d) shark

Q. 4 – Do you keep a supply of condoms:

(a) in your wallet for easy access

(b) hidden in the bathroom for a planned event

(c) in strategic places around your room and in your wallet (at all times)

(d) you rely on the man to have them

Q. 5 – Just supposing your mechanic was the fittest thing on two legs . . . and just supposing he offered to knock £100 off your bill if you . . . would you:

(a) report him to the authorities

(b) tell him off and pay the bill

(c) allow him a grope and a snog

(d) yes, and make sure he tore up the bill afterwards

Q. 6 – Which of the following is your idea of a great night out?

(a) on the prowl in bars and clubs with the girls

(b) movies, restaurant, etc. with friends

(c) bringing a guy back to yours for a wild session

(d) all the above

Q. 7 – Would all the people you'd had sex with best fit into:

(a) a four-door saloon

(b) a pick-up truck

(c) a double-decker bus

(d) an aeroplane

Q. 8 – Be honest. How many?

(a) 5–10

(b) 11–25

(c) 26–50

(d) 51 +

Q. 9 – Have you ever done it with someone you are 'just friends' with?

(a) Hell, no!

(b) I've considered it after a few drinks but never gone through with it

(c) once or twice for mutual company

(d) you have an 'arrangement' with one or two friends – you know it won't develop into anything complicated

Q. 10 – Have you ever used your sexual charms to further your career?

(a) never

(b) you've flirted to get that job

(c) it's part of your schmooze routine

(d) daily

Mostly (a)

The chance to grab quick thrills seems to be passing you by. You like to play so safe, you may never know the freewheeling sense of freedom that comes with being just a bit naughty, just once or twice. You are being a wallflower when it comes to your sex life. Next time you have the chance to let go, do it! Life's too short to always play by the rules. Maybe the introductory section to this quiz will have got you thinking about those invisible signals!

Mostly (b)

If you think you are really, really going to get away with a little harmless steaming up of the windows, you will take the plunge. You need to look both ways and pray first, but you are known to occasionally let go of the sissy ropes and follow your lust. Learn to trust your sixth sense a bit more. Don't be put off by the inner pessimist that tells you it isn't worth it. Next time you are in close proximity to an available hunk and you are picking up the right signals, don't leave it to him to do all the work; go for it and make a lasting impression!

Mostly (c)

You are not a girl to let the grass grow under your feet. 'Who knows what will happen tomorrow, so let's party today', is your motto. You were probably not a natural opportunist, but you tried it once, liked it and did it again. You get a thrill out of being a game girl and are probably rather pleased with the effectiveness of your intuition as it has proved to be right in the majority of instances. You are able to access levels of pleasure that come from having confidence and a sunny disposition. It is the case that like attracts like. The sexy persona you have created gets you positive feedback and, in turn, this filters into your psyche and enters your consciousness at a deeper level.

Mostly (d)

Never one to pass up the chance for a quick knee trembler, or full-blown orgy come to that, you are terrified only of one thing: that you might be missing out on hot horny action! You have never considered slowing down, and always have one eye open for the next best thing, even when you already have something good in your sights. I'm not sure that you even wait to pick up the signals that someone is interested in you – you show you want them and they are powerless to resist! You are like the proverbial dog with two tails. Just remember that you can only wag one at a time!

HOW SEXUALLY ADVENTUROUS ARE YOU?

When it comes to sexual adventure, like the planet itself, few things are uncharted. If you can imagine it, someone has done it, yet your own imagination may still have some undiscovered paradise that you haven't journeyed into. We are so lucky to live in an era and a part of the world that allows us the privilege of sex as play; as part of the feel-good factor of our relationships. If we are a little kinky and like dressing up in rubber or nurses' uniforms or want to try a new type of vibrator, there are any number of books and pleasant, female-friendly retail outlets and websites to cater for our tastes. This 'sex as lifestlyle' explosion has happened only in the past ten years. Prior to the 1990s, if you wanted sex toys, you would be lucky to find something that wasn't pink and nasty and sold under the counter by a sleazy guy with a mustache. Sexual experimentation isn't for everyone, of course, and there is no need to think you are 'boring' if your tastes do not roam towards the black and shiny. However, many couples find that introducing a playful element into the sexual part of their relationship can take the pressure out of performance as the focus is switched to an alternate persona or the texture of a sexy outfit. Check out how you rate in the adventure game, and read my tips for how to plan for your journey into the naughty unknown if you are feeling brave!

Q. 1 – Your partner tries to spank you during foreplay. Do you:

(a) squeal, wriggle and pretend to not want it

(b) assume an over-the-knee position and let him do his worst

(c) flee in horror

Q. 2 – Your partner wants you to watch a porn movie with him. Do you:

(a) get the popcorn ready and slip into some sexy lingerie so you're all ready for a steam session

(b) worry that you'll find it boring/offensive/ludicrous

(c) have an argument about it

Q. 3 – You find yourself in a sex shop. Do you:

(a) think it's sad that people have to rely on props and gimmicks

(b) investigate everything and buy a couple of choice items

(c) quickly grab the first vibrator you can lay your hands on and rush out, blushing

Q. 4 – A woman makes a pass at you. Are you:

(a) flattered but take a rain check

(b) flattered and take up her offer to see where it will lead

(c) shocked or revolted

Q. 5 – Your boyfriend wants you to dress up as a naughty nurse. Do you:

(a) already have an outfit and jump at the chance to be really saucy

(b) tell him it's appalling how core workers are exploited by such 'Carry On' nonsense

(c) become a little nervous about it in case you look silly

Q. 6 – How many of the following places have you had sex?

(1) in a car park

(2) in a car

(3) in the shower

(4) at the office

(5) at a party, in front of people

(6) in the woods or public park

(7) on an aeroplane

(8) in the train loos

(9) in the cinema

(10) on a fairground ride

(11) on the tube or bus

(12) near the window with the curtains open

(13) in the sea or river

(14) in a swimming pool

(15) loudly, on a hotel balcony

(16) in a bar or night club

(17) on a beach

(18) in a graveyard at night

(19) in a place of worship

(20) in a library

Q. 7 – Have you ever played watersports games?

(a) yes, it's really naughty adult fun

(b) no, but you have been curious

(c) that's disgusting!

Q. 8 – What's your idea of a fun threesome?

(a) You and two guys

(b) You, your man and another woman

(c) You, the newspaper and a cup of tea

Q. 9 – What do you think dogging is?

(a) something to do with the Kennel Club

(b) driving to car parks and letting others watch you having sex

(c) no idea

Q. 10 – Have you ever had sex with a total stranger that you've met somewhere other than a party or club, i.e. someone you met on a train?

  (a) several times

  (b) once or twice

  (c) never

Q. 11 – How many sex toys do you own?

  (a) none

  (b) one or two favourites

  (c) a cupboard full

Q. 12 – Have you ever flashed anyone from a moving vehicle?

  (a) only with your car headlights

  (b) once when you were drunk

  (c) on several occasions

Q. 13 – Have you ever used something from the fridge to apply to your body?

  (a) a carrot you know where!

  (b) ice pack on the forehead

  (c) ice cream on your breasts

Q. 14 – Have you ever demanded sex from a man?

  (a) you would never dream of it

  (b) once for the hell of it

  (c) many times as you are always so horny

Q. 15 – Have you and your partner ever invited someone else into your bed?

(a) only the cat, for a cuddle!

(b) once when you were all out of it

(c) yes, and it was mind-blowingly naughty

Q. 16 – Does the idea of going to an orgy make you feel:

(a) nauseated

(b) intrigued

(c) excited

Q. 17 – Have you ever performed a striptease?

(a) only in front of the mirror

(b) for a sexy night in with your man

(c) with tassels, stockings and an audience

Q. 18 – Some girlfriends have organised an Ann Summers party. Do you:

(a) allow yourself to be persuaded but are nervous

(b) get your chequebook ready

(c) ask if there's a Tupperware party instead

Q. 19 – You have an erotic dream about someone you fancy at work. Do you:

(a) not look them in the eye for days in case they know

(b) tell them all the details

(c) show an extra interest in them the next day

Q. 20 – Tick as many of the following as you have tried:
  (a) oral sex on a man
  (b) oral sex on a woman
  (c) anal on you
  (d) anal on someone else with a dildo
  (e) food sex
  (f) sex in a moving vehicle
  (g) sex in front of someone else
  (h) Kama Sutra

Now add up your scores
  1. a=2; b=1; c=0
  2. a=2; b=1; c=0
  3. a=0; b=2; c=1
  4. a=1; b=2; c=0
  5. a=2; b=0; c=1
  6. Score one point for 1, 2, 3, 6, 7, 8, 12, 13, 17, 15, and 2 points for 4, 5, 9, 10, 11, 14, 16, 18, 19, 20
  7. a=2; b=1; c=0
  8. a=2; b=1; c=0
  9. a=1; b=2; c=0
  10. a=2; b=1; c=0
  11. a=0; b=1; c=2
  12. a=0; b=1; c=2
  13. a=2; b=0; c=1
  14. a=0; b=1; c=2
  15. a=0; b=1; c=2
  16. a=0; b=1; c=2

17. a = 1; b = 2; c = 0
18. a = 1; b = 2; c = 0
19. a = 0; b = 2; c = 1
20. Score one point for a,e,f,h and two points for b, c, d, g

HOW ADVENTUROUS ARE YOU?

60+

You are verging on being a sex addict! Your quest for lustful encounters is not just adventurous, it's positively exhausting. You are keen to try anything and do not want to miss out on sexual escapades, even if it means risking your relationship or your dignity. It's great that you are unshockable, but make sure that your gung-ho spirit doesn't lead you into sexual danger – or boredom. If you've tried everything by the time you are 30, what's left for later? Don't forget that cultivating a sense of the forbidden can make sex immensely thrilling. If you are too much like the Martini Lady – anytime, any place, anywhere – sex won't seem as naughty after a while. Always make sure you play safe and remember to keep some treats back for a rainy day.

50–59

There is no doubting that you are an adventurous sexual being. The erotic is on your mind quite a lot, and you are keen to advertise the fact that you are a committed hedonist. You probably have a wardrobe of sexy clothes and quite a few sex toys too – and you like to parade your open-mindedness to new lovers to get them really revved up for a horny session with you. You are bold and brazen and your sexuality is high up on your priority list for the aspect of life that gets your attention. You fully appreciate how wonderful it is to be able to celebrate your femininity in a sexual way, and intend to maximise the potential for outrageously naughty conquests!

36–49

You seem to have the perfect balance of naughty and nice, being able to access your wicked side but not going too far into the realms of the bizarre. You don't do anything you are not comfortable with, but are game enough to roll with the things you know will be fun for you or will bring pleasure to your partner. You will probably have seen a few wild antics on a hen night, or had a male stripper waggle himself at close range in your direction, and it hasn't scared you. You are probably more worried about looking silly than being thought immoral. You are such a level-headed person that you are content to have the wild stuff going on in your head rather than act it out.

21–35

You know, you could get a lot of fun out of trying something different next time you have sex, or of initiating something slightly kinky into your lovemaking, but it seems you are a little shy. If you have ever dressed up in sexy underwear, you know how erotic it can feel to make love or masturbate wearing luxurious, figure-hugging clothes. Also, there is nothing perverse about a little light punishment. Try grabbing your man by the tie and leading him to the bedroom, telling him what he has to do to please you, or wearing high-heels and hold-ups one time under the duvet so that he slides in next to you and finds you dressed for sex. Life can be enhanced by discovering new ways to experience pleasure and by pushing the boundaries of one's comfort zone. The more you experiment, the more you may find out about your secret self.

0–20

It seems the naughty side of life is not something that occupies much – or any – of your time. That's cool. It's not compulsory to be a lust-crazed demoness, but if you bought this book you must be intrigued about that side of yourself. If you want to experiment more but feel nervous, maybe there is a psychological barrier holding you back, making you think there's something dirty about sex. You should check out some of the modern Kama Sutra books and play around with the idea of the erotic as something sacred. Maybe you would like sensual massage or the more gentle expressions of desire. Try experimenting with your sensual side and get into pampering yourself, opening up to all the wonderful sensations that life has to offer. Being a grown-up can be wildly exciting, and our sexual side is as valid a part of us as any other facet of our character.

HOW KINKY ARE YOU?

Everyone's a fetishist in some sense of the word. Whether it's the feel of a certain material or the preference for a particular design of car, we all make aesthetic value judgments based on our emotional responses to stimuli. Sex is not only about bodies; it's as much a cerebral activity as it is a physiological one. And kinky sex often involves putting more clothes on than it does taking them off. Think of all those straps and belts and laces that serve to constrict and bind the 'fetishistic' object, and all those materials that galvanise and sheath the body: the leather catsuits and long boots; the uniforms and accessories. When we think of kinky sex, there isn't that much nakedness going on. Objects and outré behaviour play their part, too, and many couples choose to introduce variety into their sex lives with toys, games, outfits and, most importantly, a sense that what they are doing is naughty. Being kinky is partly about allowing ourselves 'grown-up' play – it's a way of finding pleasure through experimentation; pushing the boundaries of what we're told is allowed. Kinky sex includes dressing up in erotic outfits, bondage, erotic power games, spanking, fetishism, the use of sex toys and thinking about sex as a creative act. As long as all parties are consenting, the more esoteric byways of erotic behaviour can be cathartic and even life-changing. Mutual kinky pleasure can be a way of having relationships on a more intellectual level; where the process is as pleasurable as the end result and sex becomes about much more than just grinding away in the dark! So, how kinky are you?

Tick how many of the following you have done:

(1) worn something made of rubber (washing-up gloves don't count!)

(2) dressed up in an erotic outfit for a partner

(3) tied someone up

(4) been tied up

(5) had three-in-a-bed sex

(6) performed with another girl in front of a partner

(7) used sex toys on yourself in front of a partner

(8) used sex toys on a partner

(9) worn a strap-on

(10) covered yourself in chocolate or cream and had a partner lick it off

(11) had your bottom spanked

(12) gone out intentionally without any knickers under a skirt

(13) had sex in high heels

(14) had sex in a car park

(15) had kinky Internet sex chat

(16) bought a kinky sex mag or book

(17) been handcuffed

(18) made your boyfriend wear your knickers

(19) worn a corset and stockings

(20) had an erotic piercing

(21) played around with watersports

(22) flashed yourself at passers-by

(23) shaved off all your pubic hair

(24) worn a vibrator or dildo in your knickers in a public place

(25) gone to a fetish club

How did you score?

0–4

Well, you are not really that kinky. It may never have occurred to you that you could get a sexual thrill out of anything other than making love in a skin-on-skin context. You don't need to do outrageous stuff to enjoy yourself. That's cool, but you never know what you like until you've tried it.

5–9

You certainly have an experimental side. You have a curious and wicked streak and are quite open-minded when it comes to trying things out. It is surprising just how many men like women to be bolder and dirtier, so it may be worth trying out more kinky activities and seeing how far you want to go. It's fun!

10–14

You are a game girl. You probably have some X-rated books or magazines lying around and you like to include unorthodox pleasures into your sex life. You are very comfortable being kinky and exploring all the things it is possible for an adult to do sexually. It is probably only a matter of time before you tip the balance in favour of even more curious pastimes.

15–19

You are near the top of the kinky tree. Other people's sex lives fascinate you and you always like to hear about bizarre stuff. You are very comfortable experimenting with your sexuality and are not afraid to ask for what you want. You are very open-minded and enjoy taking on different personas without being too self-conscious.

20–25

You are the pervy princess! Have you ever actually had 'normal' sex? You are either a naughty boy's dream or one scary babe! Seriously, you are a sensation-seeker who is right at home with her unusual sexuality. If you find a partner who will indulge your fantasies, you will be very happy.

SURVIVAL PACK FOR SEXUAL ADVENTURERS

1. Talk about stuff with your partner before springing a surprise on them. If you don't yet know your partner's favourite sexual archetype, ask! There's no point getting dressed up as a French maid if his thing is seeing you wearing his football kit.

2. If you are into dressing up, always go for the best quality gear you can afford. Whilst fluffy handcuffs and comedy posing pouches might seem like a good idea at the time, it's best to buy the things that are a little more authentic and well-made. You don't want your sexy clothes falling apart at a crucial moment.

3. If you are going to try spanking games, make sure you do it properly. Always aim for the lower buttock cheeks with the emphasis on the fingers, and rebound your hand away with a quick flick of the wrist. Smacking someone with a cupped palm, with your full weight behind it, is painful and annoying.

4. Never tie someone up too tightly around pulse points – and never tie anything around anyone's neck. Ever.

5. Always agree a 'safe word' – such as the name of your street – to use when things get too much for either of you.

6. Make sure if you are having sex outdoors that there are no children about. If someone complains you can find yourself in unthinkable amounts of trouble!

7. Always play safe and consensual.

8. Have a 'sex therapy' session with your partner where you take turns being the client and analyst. The

pretend power dynamic will soon become real if you get into character and can be really horny.

9. If you are going to try anal sex, never switch from the anus to the vagina – even when using a condom – as bacteria from the back passage can cause horrid infections.

10. Never insert a breakable object into any sexual orifice. If you want to be really dirty use a washed banana or courgette – and take extra care. But given the amount of fab sex toys available, you shouldn't need to raid the fruit basket!

IS IT LOVE OR LUST?

Are you at the start of something deep and meaningful or is this a bit of mutual adult fun between two highly sexed people? There's nothing wrong with the latter, as long as you both know the limitations of such an arrangement. Ask yourself these questions and see how you rate on the lust-o-meter!

Q. 1 – You were first attracted to this person's:

(a) looks

(b) talent or sense of humour

(c) personality

(d) sex drive

Q. 2 – How often do you think about sex when you are with this person?

(a) about once an hour

(b) every now and then

(c) once during the whole time you're together

(d) constantly

Q. 3 – How often could you go without sex with this person?

(a) couple of days

(b) couple of weeks

(c) couple of months

(d) couple of hours

Q. 4 – When you meet up, on average how long does it take before you are talking about sex?

(a) an hour or so

(b) a couple of hours

(c) you don't talk very often about sex

(d) minutes

Q. 5 – Have you ever told this person your sexual fantasies?

(a) yes, and he teases you about them sometimes

(b) once when you were drunk, but he hasn't mentioned them since

(c) no, you would be too shy

(d) yes, and you have both acted them out

Q. 6 – Your close friends think this person . . .

(a) is great. You were made for each other

(b) is a good sort, based on the couple of times they have met him

(c) would make a good friend

(d) doesn't exist. Your relationship is based purely on sexual, not social, activity

Q. 7 – What's a typical evening for you both?

(a) meal and a movie or gig with drinks and chat afterwards

(b) something you both enjoy doing

(c) sports or social

(d) unadulterated private pleasures

Q. 8 – What is the main benefit this person gives you?

(a) love and security

(b) laughter and good times

(c) companionship

(d) great orgasms

Q. 9 – If, for whatever reason, this person couldn't fulfil your sexual needs. Would you:

(a) stay with it. You are bound by so much more than physical antics

(b) be tempted to cheat once or twice, but strive to save the relationship

(c) not be bothered as sex isn't that important to you anyway

(d) have to admit it is over as it is really important to you

Q. 10 – When you meet up, what's the first thing you do?

(a) kiss and cuddle

(b) crack jokes

(c) talk about your respective days

(d) tell each other about your sexual feelings

So is it love, lust or good old friendship?

Mostly (a)

This relationship is governed by love, which doesn't mean that it is totally platonic, but that the feelings run deeper than your mutual physical satisfaction. You care for each other, are friends *and* lovers, and the levels of intimacy and trust at work here mean that you will probably be together for a long time.

Mostly (b)

The predominant aspect here is friendship. You get on really well with this person, and look forward to sharing good times with them. As to whether anything more meaningful can develop is up to your individual requirements and chemistry. If one of you is holding back from commitment, then you need to explore what it is you fear from moving forward with the relationship. Alternatively, you could form a deeper bond with some mind-blowing sessions in the bedroom and hope for the best.

Mostly (c)

Face it, you make better friends than lovers. You have somehow got it together and are getting on fine, but the sexual aspect of things is not exactly first thing on your menu. If you are unable to proceed with a physical relationship because of shyness or lack of sexual motivation for whatever reason, perhaps you should consider that it may be better for you to cut the boyfriend/

girlfriend pretensions and just stay pals. Someone more suitable as a sexual partner will come along soon enough.

Mostly (d)

The signs point to lust being the prime motivator in this relationship. You are driven by a physical craving and do not seem interested in allowing anything non-sexual to enter the equation. It is rare that one is able to maintain such an arrangement for very long, as unbridled lust tends to dwindle over time, so enjoy this gratifying, single-interest partnership while it lasts and look at it as an opportunity to learn about the deeper aspects of your sexuality.

8. THE BIG O

Let's face it, it's wonderful. The female orgasm serves no purpose other than giving a woman pure, unadulterated pleasure. Once we discover what that tiny little button can do, a whole new world of delights awaits us. The clitoris is much bigger than you may think. The part that we can touch is only the tip of a much bigger (forked!) organ of nerves that measures up to four inches inside ourselves. Women have the potential to become multi-orgasmic, able to climax again and again without having to rest for half an hour in between. Despite what you see in movies, female orgasm during intercourse alone is very unusual. The percentages vary, but I would say all statistics agree that over 80 per cent of women have to have some clitoral stimulation in order to climax. If the clitoris was inside the vagina, then that percentage would of course drop significantly, but most women would say that the design is just fine as it stands. Having someone continue to thrust away at the clitoris just after we have orgasmed would be painful.

Female masturbation isn't a taboo topic of conversation anymore but it is something that most of us prefer to keep private. Even the closest girlfriends would be uncomfortable swapping tips for their favourite methods with each other. But women really have the upper hand on this issue. There is still a huge mystique around it: guys are seen as sad for doing it whereas women are seen as being 'in touch with their sensual selves'. Ninety-nine per cent of men are aroused by the thought of or sight of a masturbating woman. Pubescent boys can't believe women do it; and grown-up men are fascinated by the mechanics of how they do it.

We each individually know what works best for us, and once we get into a groove we can be reluctant to change. Some women, for example, cannot climax with their legs apart; some can come only while lying on their front, or back, or whatever. You may be happy using your tried and tested masturbation technique, but it can be fun to experiment with new ones. It is also useful to be adaptable so we can adjust to the challenges of new lovers.

But what if your orgasm is eluding you? Well, a small revolution has occurred in British sexual culture over the last ten years, namely the availability of sex toys designed for women. Whereas once sex shops were off-limits to females, most towns now have a female-friendly sex shop that is bright and cheerful, carrying a mind-boggling selection of funky-coloured, twirling, buzzing tricks designed to help tease the most stubborn big Os from the shyest girls. Orgasm is primarily psychological, but the sexual gadgetry that has hit the high street in recent years can really help with the back-up.

OK, let's test your O quotient

Q. 1. – Is having an orgasm for you:

(a) the most important part of sex

(b) the icing on a very nice cake

(c) something you wished happened more often

(d) something you dream of but have only managed once or twice

Q. 2 – How often do you masturbate?

(a) once a day or more

(b) three times a week

(c) once a week

(d) hardly ever

Q. 3 – Do you have any sex toys?

(a) a whole range of vibrators and dildos

(b) a couple of funky things that do the trick

(c) one discreet little vibrator

(d) certainly not!

Q. 4 – Have you ever orgasmed during your sleep?

(a) it happens a few times a year

(b) occasionally

(c) once or twice

(d) it's never happened to you

Q. 5 – Do you find it easiest to orgasm in front of your partner:

(a) if you do it yourself

(b) if he does it for you

(c) not that easy but you get there in the end

(d) you could never orgasm in front of anyone else

Q. 6 – How many of the following have you used to bring you to orgasm? (score one point for each)

(a) erotic fiction

(b) porn magazine

(c) sexy video

(d) true confessions stories

(e) other people's fantasies

(f) your own dirty mind

(g) phone sex

(h) vibrator or sex toy

(i) shower nozzle or jacuzzi jet

(j) washing machine

Q. 7 – How many of the following have you ever done as you've orgasmed? (score one point for each)

(a) burst out laughing

(b) burst into tears

(c) shouted

(d) bitten or scratched your partner

(e) bitten or scratched yourself

(f) ejaculated (it is possible!)

(g) lost consciousness

(h) declared undying love

(i) sworn out loud

(j) fainted

Q. 8 – Was your first orgasm:

(a) something you read about and practised alone

(b) with a partner – again, something you were both aiming for

(c) a total shock; you didn't know what was happening

(d) you're still to have it

Q. 9 – Which of the following do you prefer to do?

(a) orgasm from masturbation

(b) orgasm during intercourse

(c) orgasm from oral sex

(d) any orgasm will do!

Q. 10 – Is your orgasm usually:

(a) body ripplingly intense

(b) waves of pleasure that course through you

(c) a slight tremor between the legs

(d) don't know

How did you score?

1. a = 4; b = 3; c = 2; d = 1
2. a = 4; b = 3; c = 2; d = 1
3. a = 4; b = 3; c = 2; d = 1
4. a = 4; b = 3; c = 2; d = 1
5. a = 4; b = 3; c = 2; d = 1
6. Score a point for each one
7. Score a point for each one
8. a = 3; b = 4; c = 2; d = 1
9. a = 2; b = 3; c = 1; d = 4
10. a = 4; b = 3; c = 2; d = 1

How was it for you?

41–52

Big Bang. You really love your orgasms! You are totally at ease with your sexuality and are at the lucky stage of having reached your prime orgasmic potential. Your partner is a lucky guy! Every time he sees you climax his ego will get a boost. To be as orgasmic as you are sends out the message that you are something of a sex goddess. And there is nothing more attractive to a man than a woman who is so completely happy in herself and sensually motivated. You are revelling in your femininity and womanliness, and giving your man (or men) and yourself something to smile about.

31–40

Rocket woman. You are blazing towards being super orgasmic. You know what you like and pretty much get it. You might like to have a go at finding new ways to come; maybe treat yourself to one of the great new sex toys that are available. You know how to enjoy your body and that of your partner. Maybe you have settled into a routine with your partner that you can spice up with different games or positions.

21–30

Starry night. You enjoy sex but are not getting the most out of your orgasm potential. Maybe you feel a little shy of expressing what it is you really want. In order to improve your O quotient, you need to relax a little more, maybe read some sexy stories or try and write one. Experiment with masturbation at different times of the day and work out when you feel most horny. If it is at inconvenient times, when your lover isn't around, try telling him about it, and agree to send sexy thoughts to each other at that time. Then, when you meet up later, the atmosphere will sizzle with expectation.

10–20

Mission impossible. Well, you have everything to look forward to. Right now something is preventing you from accessing your ultimate pleasure zone. You seem to find it difficult to relax; maybe deep breathing exercises will help, combined with flexing your pelvic (Kegel) floor muscles. Take time to pamper yourself. Spend a day treating yourself to life's little luxuries and learn that it is perfectly OK to have erotic thoughts. Try letting your mind wander into the naughty zone. Read some erotic stories or enjoy thinking of yourself as an innocent maiden with the whole of her sexual life in front of her. Check out my tips for sexual confidence on page 53.

ORGASM MYSTERIES, PROBLEMS AND SOLUTIONS

'I'm too ashamed to tell my partner how to make me come.'

Most women have faked orgasm at some point in their lives. The majority of men – who, of course cannot get away with such a thing – are wounded by the thought that they are unable to make it happen for their partners. But they are not mind-readers; if your boyfriend is not touching you in the right way, educate him! There is no point being shy at this stage. You've had his penis inside you; how much ruder does it need to be before you can speak freely about what you want? At this stage of the game, the majority of men are more aroused by a woman letting go than her trying to remain demure, so go for it! If you shock him, or he refuses to do it, then he needs to grow up!

'I can orgasm easily alone, but find it really difficult to do it in front of my boyfriend.'

The orgasm can be highly elusive when it becomes an imperative; the more you chase it, the fainter the chance of it happening becomes. The occasions when orgasm seems to be easier are the first time you have sex with someone and when you know each other really well. It's when you are in the one to six month stage of a relationship that most orgasm difficulties occur. This is when we are likely to be at our most self-aware within the relationship, not knowing if it's going to be a long-term thing, which makes it harder to let go and be as down and dirty as we need to be in order to come freely. It's about trust, too. You need to be able to trust your new partner with your sexual profile − allowing someone who you don't yet know really well to have access to the most personal information about yourself. If you cannot let go enough yet to climax under his hand, then touch yourself until you feel you are almost ready, then get him to finish you off. You could even use his erect penis on your clitoris to do the job. If you are a little tense about orgasming in front of someone, you could try the old favourite and do it in the dark, under the covers. Even though it will still be his hand between your legs, you will feel protected and secure. Lighten up. Relish your 'naughty time' as if you were getting away with something you shouldn't.

'We keep trying to have simultaneous orgasms but just can't time them right.'

The simultaneous orgasm is a bit of a movie cliché, to be honest. Not many people manage to perfect this, and for one very good reason: it's better to have them separately so you can fully enjoy your own as well as enjoying seeing your partner having his − which you would miss in its full glory if you were busy thrashing around yourself. It's good to 'do a double' at least once in your relationship, but once you have ticked that box your time is better spent making your individual ones better!

'My boyfriend has the opposite of premature ejaculation, and goes on for so long that I get bored.'

If the words, 'I'll make love to you all night, baby' fill you with dread, take heart. Men often labour under the false impression that women want them to last ages. Maybe it's a hangover from listening to too many cheesy R'n'B lyrics, but the reality is that most women prefer a session to last thirty minutes to a couple of hours, max. Holding off one's climax is all well and good up to a point, but most of us are too busy for tantric shenanigans. If you're not a girl who likes all-night loving, all the time, tell him early on in your relationship so he knows the score. But do mention it in a light-hearted way.

If there seems to be a genuine problem, and the guy actually can't come in under an hour, he may have some psychological blockage that's preventing him from letting go.

Orgasm – male and female – is triggered by the build-up of naughty thoughts that get more and more concentrated until one is pushed over the edge. You need to let him know it's OK to go wild with you. It's highly unlikely that he would take so long to come when he masturbates. Tell him to think about whatever it is that gets him there when he touches himself. Try talking dirty to him. The thing not to do is yawn, look at your watch or fall asleep!

'I orgasm in my sleep. How on earth can this happen without touching myself?'

It happens to teenage boys a lot but can also happen to fully grown women. Medieval theologians posited the existence of an 'incubus' – a demon who had intercourse with women while they slept. (The 'succubus' is the equivalent for men.) It is amazing to think that the unconscious mind is so incredibly powerful that it can bring a person to a hands-off climax that will wake them up. When we are lucky enough to have an erotic dream that doesn't get interrupted by something surreal, our uncensored desire allows us total psychological immersion in the phenomenon. Consequently dream orgasms are often stronger than waking ones. A study published in the *Journal of Sex Research* in 1986 found that 85 per cent of women who had experienced nocturnal orgasms had done so by the age of 21. In addition, women who have orgasms during sleep usually have them several times a year. Fewer than 10 per cent of women, compared to 50 per cent of males, report having night-time orgasms more than five times a year. Men often experience their first orgasm during a wet dream, but women rarely have them until they have had orgasm by some other means first. Wet dreams usually make little impression on men, but women sometimes have quite vivid sexual dreams in connection with nocturnal orgasms; so much so that the dreamer may believe she has actually had sex! The ability to fantasise to orgasm without physically masturbating is exceedingly rare. In psychological terms, it's called 'psychic masturbation', yet I don't believe that anyone except the most expert tantric practitioner would be able to replicate this experience while consciously trying to do so.

'I can only orgasm when I think about really hard-core fantasies, such as forced sex or gang-bangs. Is there something wrong with me?'

Not at all. Our fantasies are a private matter, and you are under no obligation to confess them to anyone else unless you are 110 per cent confident that they won't react badly to them. The 'rape' fantasy has provoked heated debate and is a controversial subject that has been analysed perfectly well by the sex therapist Betty Dodson who said that, in your imagination you may be the 'victim', but you are also 'the rapist'. Having fantasies about rough men doesn't mean that you want to be subjugated in real life. The imagination is inherently transgressive; our subconscious mind will throw up all manner of wild and scary archetypes and scenarios – partly as a means of getting us psychologically used to 'bad' characters so we can spot them in real life, and partly as a compensatory device to balance our 'good' conscious mind. The human mind will fantasise about what it is not supposed to – what is repressed – and this is perfectly natural. There is much that lies between stimulus and response. If you are stimulated by the idea of sexually dominant rough types, you become aroused: a simple, cause and effect equation. Yet the reason these archetypes are arousing to you lies somewhere deeper – in your own personal sexual psychology. We grow up with stories featuring scary monsters, 'baddies', etc. We like being scared, but knowing that we are tucked up safe in bed where nothing can harm us. When we mature, the fairy stories become sexual fantasies, but their formula remains similar. Fear and arousal are very closely linked. Pleasure is both desirable *and* forbidden. No matter how anodyne most magazine articles on sex seem to be, the reality is that many of us are turned on by what we are not supposed to be, which is naughty . . . ergo, enjoyable. Just enjoy your fantasies but I recommend you keep them to yourself. You wouldn't want your partner to try and arrange for them to be made real!

MADDIE'S SEX AND RELATIONSHIPS SURVIVAL GUIDE

This section of the book is like a condensed problem page for those emergency situations that we may have to deal with at some point in our lives – such as the gnarly problem of jealousy and what to do if you think you have a dysfunctional lover. It can be a jungle out there as far as dating and relating goes. There are marauding predators, wild animals and traps around every corner – not to mention a few poisonous snakes along the way. You need a personal sexual survival guide to ensure that you stay ahead of the game. On the battlefield of sexual relationships, you need as much weaponry in your arsenal as possible and good radar for anticipating trouble. Relationships are a competitive business; there is always the worry that someone younger, prettier and more beguiling will come along and whisk your man from under your nose. We don't dwell on these possibilities as that would drive us crazy, but most of us at some point will have had to face the indignity of watching our partner flirting with another woman or seeing him backed into a corner by an unscrupulous *femme fatale* who gets a kick out of seducing other people's boyfriends. We can be comforted by knowing that it works both ways: in his mind, there's always a hunk waiting in the wings with a bulging wallet and lunch box and a flasher car than his.

Our relationships encounter obstacles that have the potential to wound our egos. But if we know how to handle the rough patches with skill and cunning we can steer through them, win the day and retain our dignity and our sexual confidence. Unfortunately, it seems to be the human condition that we learn these lessons slowly, by trial and error. How many of us think back to our first relationships and cringe at how we behaved: how we would approach things differently; how we wouldn't have thrown a drunken strop in the high street or burst into tears in front of all our friends at that party. Between the genders, we have enough sexual neuroses to keep an army of psychotherapists in yachts. Yet we each have the ability to maintain and repair our relationships perfectly well ourselves. All we need is a practical attitude, a good sense of timing and a sprinkling of sensitivity.

Each gender has its weak spot. Men are particularly sensitive about performance, penis size and sexual experience. Women tend to be worried about body shape, the firmness of their breasts and whether their partner fancies them enough. Our fragile egos take a daily pounding from all those images of perfection that serve to remind us we are less than A-list – whether financially, physically or professionally. These days, as many guys are having 'six-pack paranoia' as women are stressing about the size of their bums. Modern life requires us to be superhuman – juggling work or study with hectic social or family lives, and trying to make ends meet *as well* as looking drop-dead gorgeous. It's a tall order, and not surprising that we often find ourselves unloading our problems onto our partners and expecting too much of each other.

While we are on the subject of expecting too much, we are also becoming increasingly materialistic, but we might be the last of the big spenders. Recent studies show that borrowing is at an all-time high and the UK is some £930 billion in debt. It is difficult not to desire the celebrity lifestyle that is paraded in front of us everywhere we turn. We all like a bit of luxury, but if you have Prada tastes and Primark wages, you will be living in a permanent state of unfulfilment – not to mention financial trouble. You may be wondering what this has to do with your sex life. The answer is, probably a lot more than you imagine. As society makes more demands of us, we in turn can transfer our burden onto those closest to us and demand more of them. We have all become obsessed with targets. Parents expect their children to be super-achievers; bosses expect their employees to work longer hours for no extra pay, and many of us see our partners as being directly responsible for our happiness. Maybe we want commitment earlier than our partner feels comfortable with, or maybe our partner displays what we think are unrealistic expectations of us.

When I am counselling couples, I often see an imbalance of desires – a contest of wills that is a recipe for discord. Usually one partner wants more commitment and the other wants more space. This romantic dichotomy is used as material for countless sitcoms, books and movies, the inevitable outcome usually being the capitulation of the man's freedom in favour of the woman getting what she wants – although there are plenty of real-life circumstances where men are the prime movers in a couple settling down. As long as both parties are happy, this is cool. Yet I increasingly believe we need to pull back from fast-tracking our relationships into places where they have not yet naturally evolved. We need to downshift our expectations of others and breathe some air into our relationships, giving them a chance to grow organically. So much of the disharmony between couples arises out of one person's impatience.

As far as possible, we want to keep the intensity in our relationships centred on the pleasure principle. However, there is the likelihood that, at some point, things will 'go wrong' in the bedroom. Maybe it will be an argument over sexual needs: perhaps your partner may want you to do something you are not happy with; maybe you haven't had sex for three months because one of you is too stressed out. Whatever it is, be assured that 90 per cent of couples will have the occasional sexual hiccup. This is natural. Humans are complex creatures with elaborate histories and active inner lives. Our unconscious minds and psyches are always on overdrive, even when we are asleep. Given the stresses and strains of modern life, many of us find it difficult to relax and switch off from worrying about stuff. Our ancestors may have physically worked themselves to a premature old age, but today's hectic lifestyle is proving to be psychologically more stressful. Balancing the work/play dilemma is top of many people's agendas and quality time has become the contemporary Holy Grail. This obviously includes sex. This should be our 'adult playtime' – it should not be a chore or something we feel we have to do. Many people tell me they are too tired for love. At the end of a hard-working day and a challenging public transport situation many of us are flopping exhausted on the sofa or hitting the pillow and instantly crashing out. This means that we are not getting the playtime we deserve and need – the recreational part of life that is essential for happiness.

When a relationship hiccup comes along, if you are not a hundred per cent relaxed and confident in your sexual self, it is easy to blow minor things out of proportion or take the blame for something going wrong and fall into the spiral of low self-esteem – the bedrock of modern psychological distress. How many of us have fallen into the trap of needing to be told again and again that our partner loves us? We ask those terribly loaded questions: do you love me? You don't love me anymore, do you? Why don't you love me anymore? All this serves to do is back our partner into a corner and load them with the responsibility of our happiness. That is not their job. If something is going off track in your relationship, the worst thing you can do is pester the other person for demonstrations of affection. Such displays should come naturally. I have heard heart-wrenching tales of the impossible lengths some women will go to in order to get the affection they need from their partners. But the more desperately you search for love, the more elusive it can be. Although we feel that we have to make a monumental effort to get what we need, often the best things come to us once we have stopped striving for them.

If you feel exhausted and this is having a knock-on effect on your relationship, try some of the tips in the Sexual Confidence Masterclass section on page 53, especially tips 6 and 7. Spend at least one evening a week pampering yourself – that doesn't include watching TV. Make sure you are eating healthily and getting exercise. Even a few lengths of the swimming pool after work a couple of times a week will help you to feel more balanced and grounded. And – I cannot stress this enough times – take up yoga. If you only do one form of exercise, make it this one. For emotional, physical and spiritual well-being, it cannot be beaten.

This next quiz will help you analyse how healthy your relationship is. If you are not in a relationship at the moment, then rate yourself according to how things progressed last time you were. You may even be able to identify what went wrong and learn to deal with those issues next time. For the purposes of convenience when the questions mention 'calling' someone, this can mean text, email or phone.

HOW HEALTHY IS YOUR RELATIONSHIP?

Q. 1 – The first time you had sex, was it:
  (a) mutual – you were both hot for each other
  (b) OK – something to pass the time
  (c) hard work – you felt that you had to convince him it was a good idea

Q. 2 – Afterwards, did you feel it was:
  (a) fun – you laughed a lot together and had a big smile on your faces for a week
  (b) sweet – you didn't set the world on fire, but it was affectionate
  (c) pants – it was disappointing

Q. 3 – How did you meet up again:
  (a) one of you called the other within five days
  (b) you ran into each other again by chance
  (c) one of you called the other the next day and asked when you were meeting up again

Q. 4 – After going out with each other for three months, were you:
  (a) still on a casual basis
  (b) inseparable
  (c) feeling either that you were making all the effort or a little hemmed in

Q. 5 – How often do you argue?
  (a) never
  (b) occasionally
  (c) it's a constant game of one-upmanship

Q. 6 – How often do you feel you are being taken for granted?

(a) never

(b) occasionally

(c) often

Q. 7 – For the most part, would you say your relationship is:

(a) loving and affectionate

(b) convenient and functional

(c) tired and emotional

Q. 8 – You each have different plans for the weekend. Do you:

(a) agree to have different weekends

(b) one of you adjusts their plans

(c) spend the weekend arguing and do neither

Q. 9 – At a party, one of you is really enjoying it but the other wants to leave. Do you:

(a) leave together anyway. There'll always be another party

(b) agree to stay another thirty minutes as a compromise

(c) argue and leave separately

Q. 10 – When you arrange to meet somewhere, do you usually:

(a) arrive at the agreed time

(b) one of you is usually late

(c) it's always a casual arrangement so you don't usually make plans

Q. 11 – He's off on a lads' weekend. Do you feel:

    (a) miserable – you hate not spending your free time together

    (b) OK, but a little left out

    (c) relieved – you can have a girls' weekend

Q. 12 – When it comes to picking up the tab in a restaurant, do you usually pay:

    (a) the full whack

    (b) nothing

    (c) a fairly divided amount according to your respective earnings

Q. 13 – Have you ever surprised him with a gift?

    (a) often

    (b) once or twice

    (c) no, it wouldn't be appropriate

Q. 14 – When it comes to managing money does he:

    (a) let you make your own decisions

    (b) moan at you for your spendthrift ways

    (c) gently advise you what's best

Q. 15 – How reliable is he at keeping to arrangements?

    (a) he often changes plans or lets you down

    (b) he's always punctual and reliable

    (c) he sometimes forgets

Q. 16 – He has an orgasm but you don't. Does he:

(a) try to make it happen, baby

(b) take it as a personal insult

(c) not even notice

Q. 17 – He wants to do something in bed that you're not into. Do you:

(a) do it anyway to keep him happy

(b) say you'd rather not, confident it won't affect your relationship

(c) do it, then make him do something you want

Q. 18 – Have you ever drawn attention to your imperfections (spots/weird toes/flab, etc.)?

(a) you joke about it

(b) you often ask if he still fancies you in spite of them

(c) you don't have any and, even if you did, he should like you the way you are

Q. 19 – Generally, in the sack, do you feel that:

(a) you get mutual pleasure

(b) the pleasure seems to be all his

(c) the pleasure is mostly yours

Q. 20 – Have you ever asked him if he loves you?

(a) you don't need to because you know he does

(b) you want him to tell you without you having to ask

(c) you often find yourself asking this

How did you score?

1. a=3; b=2; c=1	2. a=3; b=2; c=1
3. a=2; b=1; c=3	4. a=2; b=3; c=1
5. a=3; b=2; c=1	6. a=3; b=2; c=1
7. a=3; b=2; c=1	8. a=3; b=2; c=1
9. a=3; b=2; c=1	10. a=3; b=2; c=1
11. a=1; b=2; c=3	12. a=1; b=2; c=3
13. a=3; b=2; c=1	14. a=3; b=1; c=2
15. a=1; b=3; c=2	16. a=3; b=1; c=2
17. a=1; b=3; c=2	18. a=2; b=1; c=3
19. a=3; b=1; c=2	20. a=3; b=2; c=1

50+

Your relationship is at peak fitness. You have a sound, healthy idea of yourselves as autonomous individuals who respect each other and are affectionate without being needy. You discuss things, are able to nip any relationship trouble in the bud, and each of you knows how the other feels about a particular issue. If you fall out over something, it is likely that you will diffuse any antagonism with a joke or by a hot session in bed. You laugh a lot together – the best sign of compatibility and the basis for a long-lasting friendship or relationship. You feel that you work well as a team and, most importantly, you trust each other.

40–49

Your relationship is healthy, but it could use the occasional workout. There is sometimes a slight imbalance in the way each of you views the world and your commitment to each other. One of you seems to be putting in more effort than the other to keep things together. Next time you hit a rocky patch, agree to set aside some non-judgmental time to talk things through without feeling as if you are in competition with each other. Maybe one of you is wary of letting the other see the real person. Whilst it is fine to present a persona to our colleagues and the acquaintance down the road, we shouldn't be afraid to let our partners see the real person. One of you needs to relax a little more and trust your heart and your true feelings. Open up a little more and things will only get better!

30–39

Your relationship is a bit out of condition. Things have got into a rut and need to be unstuck. All is not lost, but you need to take a long cold look at the situation and work out where things have gone wrong and what you can do to improve it. One of you isn't getting what they want from the relationship and is feeling cheated. Maybe one of you is putting too much pressure on the other. This is a common occurrence. If we are lacking something in our lives, it is very convenient to pile all our unfulfilled desires onto a partner or spouse. This can be a 'false economy', as ultimately we are all responsible for our own happiness. Whichever of you is being needy or frosty should look at when you originally started withdrawing affection and why. You need to talk to each other more, and learn that it is OK to pursue individual lives. The strongest relationships tend to be the ones where each person maintains his/her own friends and interests.

20–29

Call the doctor! You need to do some emergency surgery to get your relationship back on a healthy footing

– unless, of course, your chemistry is clashing so badly that it cannot be made better. You have to ask yourself, when you first got together, was it a mutually happy occasion? Did you feel good afterwards, or are you staying together just because you can't summon up the courage to end it? It seems that one of you is taking the other for granted. Unless you try a more healthy approach to this relationship, things are going to get toxic pretty fast. None of us should have to tolerate disrespect. If you are putting out for your man and he can't even be bothered to turn up or doesn't care about your pleasure, dump that chump and move on!

TEN TOUGH RELATIONSHIP QUESTIONS

1. **Are you a doormat?** No one should put up with disrespect or being taken for granted. If your man lets you down really badly, i.e. doesn't turn up to your birthday party, or stands you up without warning you he can't make a date more than once, there is something seriously wrong. Don't become some-one's doormat. Stand up for yourself and get shot of that loser.

2. **Are you both making compromises?** Don't always be the one to give in to his plans or, conversely, don't have a hissy fit if you don't get your own way all the time. This said, we shouldn't compromise ourselves to the hilt. There is no need to be joined at the hip with your partner. It doesn't matter if you attend different parties one night, or go to the movies with your friends instead of him. Let each other off the leash occasionally!

3. **How much fun you are sharing?** When was the last time either of you laughed at the other's

anecdotes? Being with someone should be about fun as much as commitment. Laughing together is the best sign of a healthy relationship, keeps us young and injects a dynamic energy into our partnerships.

4. **Do you still fancy each other?** This is a tricky one to be honest about but it is really important. If you sense that the sexual spark has gone from one or both sides of the partnership, address it. Don't sign the joint mortgage if you haven't had sex for six months!

5. **Are you arguing about money?** Economic strain puts the frighteners on relationships worse than an affair. Try to avoid getting into debt – especially to your partner. If your man is constantly critical of the way you manage money, beware, as deeper commitment will make him even more nit-picking. Men just don't understand that a girl has to treat herself once in a while!

6. **Are you faithful?** There are many reasons why a person in a relationship might explore someone else 'on the side'. An affair need not be the end of a relationship and, in some cases, may even save it. Obviously a safe-sex only rule has to apply to extra activity. The greater the level of commitment to your partner, the more that is at risk. You need to search your own soul for how they would feel if they found out. If you have to have an affair, at least make sure it is with someone your partner has never met. Getting off with his best mate is unforgivable.

7. **Will you be there for each other?** When life throws up horrible unforeseen difficulties such as illness, bereavement, redundancy, etc. do you think your partner would be sympathetic to your circumstances? Is there an unconditional love at the basis of your relationship that means you can trust that

person for their support? And would you do the same for them?

8. **How's your social life?** As much as we love our partners, never let your friends fade into being a distant memory – you never know when you might need them. Make sure you meet up with them sometimes without your partner. If you maintain an active contact with friends, you will have more to chat about to your boyfriend. Think of the middle-aged couple who barely say a word to each other in the restaurant . . . these are the people who never kept their own social lives.

9. **How is your sex life?** Are you still talking to each other about what you like and sharing your erotic thoughts? Don't let complacency creep in to your bedroom. Although the initial 'must have you now' imperative wanes after the first couple of years of most relationships, it can be replaced with a deep trust and an intense erotic love that can last decades.

10. **Have you let yourself go?** Many people relax a bit too much once they are going 'long-term' or living together. If you stop making an effort to look good at *any* time, or your domestic habits slide into slobsville, don't be surprised if your partner's eye roves elsewhere. This works both ways . . . you owe it to the both of you to stay a good-looking couple!

HAVE A RELATIONSHIP REVIEW

Like a car, a relationship needs a service now and then to keep the parts in working order. We know that when we ignore the horrible rattling sound in the engine, the car will let us down when we need it most. Many modern couples have a 'relationship review' session twice a year that lasts a couple of hours. This is where things can be discussed and problems aired with the accent on sensitivity and positive results. Where niggles are identified, resolutions are reached. These are not slanging matches, and shouldn't be used as an excuse to make the other person feel bad. Although it sounds horribly businesslike or even scary, most couples find that these sessions improve their relationships. Even if nothing is off-key in your partnership, you can spend the time saying all the things you like about each other. You should be doing that regularly anyway. But if you have never had a relationship review, set a date about two weeks in advance and take the time to note down all the things you love and like about being with that person. Then make a list (ideally a short one!) of things where you think there is room for improvement. Set a day when you will be undisturbed, and when neither of you has to be anywhere else, when there is no pressure for time.

When it comes to the review, try following these simple rules

1. Switch off all extraneous interference: TV, radio, stereo, etc.

2. Don't let alcohol play a big part. Keep it to one bottle of wine at most.

3. Don't use it as a 'blame or shame' session. Always keep the accent on the positive.

4. Decide who is going to go first. Agree to hear what the other person has to say and don't interrupt them. Wait until they have finished before replying.

5. Always begin by talking about the things you love about your partner and the relationship.

6. Be sensitive. If there are criticisms, think of a way to approach the subject that isn't going to make the other person feel persecuted. Read what you have to say beforehand and imagine your partner saying it to you. How would you feel?

7. Don't criticise personal things that cannot be changed, i.e. penis size, family background, etc.

8. Be brief! Don't go on and on about something as this may make your partner feel upset.

9. Where a repeat problem is identified, for example, your partner 'always wants to leave parties early' or one of you is constantly doing themselves down to the other, e.g. moaning 'I'm really fat', try to find solutions rather than continuing to repeat the behaviour. If, for instance, you can pinpoint the type of parties your partner isn't comfortable at, go to them by yourself. There is nothing worse than forcing someone to be somewhere or do something they don't want to. What is bad is straining to keep up appearances – a terrible rut that some couples get into. If one of you has a self-esteem problem, try the sexual confidence masterclass or work out what it was that made you first feel like this and talk about it. Don't just whinge – act to change what is bothering you!

10. Don't let your review spiral into an argument. Always end your session with a cuddle and the agreement to commit to making the relationship work.

THE GREEN-EYED MONSTER

We have all felt it at some point: the sickening rage and jealousy that makes our blood boil and can turn us into a potential bunny boiler in our partner's eyes. A good friend of mine once became so obsessed with a woman whom she thought was trying to seduce her boyfriend, that she would follow this woman and park outside her house so she could monitor her movements. She had never been a jealous type prior to that one person coming into their lives. She suddenly became obsessed. Her boyfriend – a very easy-going guy – was mildly flattered by the attention the new woman was giving him, but had no intention of acting upon it. But this was not enough for my friend, who became convinced that he was thinking about the woman during their lovemaking, and could not relax when they had sex. Consequently, she stopped having orgasms and she thought his were prompted by fantasies about the other woman. She would pester him about his opinion of her: did he fancy her? Did he think her breasts were better than hers? Did he want to have sex with her? and so on until she became a nervous wreck and he stopped wanting to go out with her. It was only through counselling that my friend was able to work out why this particular woman had posed such a threat to her. As it turned out, the woman married a wealthy investment broker and moved away, and my friend and her boyfriend are still together. However, her jealousy almost killed their relationship.

If you or your partner is easily roused to jealousy, the root cause should be identified as soon as possible and treated. It can be an extremely unattractive feature. Obsessive attention to how your partner is relating to others, seeing any available person of the same sex as an instant threat, or worrying needlessly on unfounded grounds your partner is being unfaithful, is a bad use of energy. And, rather than securing their desire for you, your constant checking up on them will most likely drive them away. We come back to the point about self-esteem. If you feel confident within yourself, you won't feel threatened by the first attractive woman that starts talking to your boyfriend. If you are lacking that basic confidence and feel threatened, you should try to work out what is missing from your life or why you automatically assume the worst will happen.

Some people seem to be born pessimists or worriers. Even those with material comforts fret unnecessarily that things will go wrong or threaten their security. They can never fully enjoy the present as they are constantly concerned what others are thinking about them or what threat is lurking around the corner. For whatever reason, such people feel self-conscious or vulnerable, and this can destroy their spirit. Although stress levels are high in the modern world, it is beneficial to recognise life's challenges as opportunities – and not look at the opportunities as challenges. The jealous person will be someone who has difficulty relaxing; who is more prone to worry and stress than is average, and who is likely to have low self-esteem. As in the case of my friend, jealousy can threaten the stability of a relationship and, in extreme cases, lead to aggressive or violent behaviour. If a person feels psychologically vulnerable, they can feel backed into a corner and get locked into a cycle of damaging behaviour: perceived threat + fear + anger = jealousy. If alcohol is added to this cycle, the consequences can be unpleasant and uncivilised. It is important to keep a lid on that green-eyed monster.

Check your green-eye rating

Q. 1 – Have you ever done any of the following? Tick as many as you have done or tick none if you are not guilty!

(a) looked through your partner's diary

(b) checked his emails

(c) called his mobile when he's told you he's out with his buddies

(d) quizzed his friends to find out where he went on his night out

(e) been waiting for him at his place when he returns after a night out

Q. 2 – At a party, your partner is spending a long time talking with an attractive woman. What's your reaction?

(a) you find the nearest attractive man and start flirting with him

(b) so what? You know that you'll be going home together at the end of the party

(c) you sulk in the corner, unable to relax

(d) you go over and introduce yourself

(e) you cause some kind of a scene

Q. 3 – Your partner's phone is constantly on voicemail over the course of an evening. Do you assume:

(a) he's forgotten to charge his phone

(b) he's out with his buddies and will call you when he gets a moment

(c) he's losing interest in you

(d) he's working too hard

(d) he's out shagging some hot new babe

Q. 4 – Your partner ogles a woman in the street. What's your reaction?

(a) join in the ogling for fun

(b) it's natural, all men do it

(c) it's a display of weakness that disappoints you

(d) you are cross and a little hurt

(e) you are furious

Q. 5 – You find your partner has porn mags or dvds. What do you think about that?

(a) you don't mind at all

(b) you find it uncomfortable because it's 'not very nice'

(c) you feel threatened by it as the models are all so perfect

(d) you feel a little sad that he is so predictable

(e) you are fairly worried and think that you should be enough for him

Q. 6 – Your boyfriend goes on a stag weekend in Amsterdam. Do you:

(a) worry he's going to overdo it on the partying

(b) wish you were going on the hen weekend

(c) ask him to call or email you at least once

(d) worry that he'll be tempted to stray

(e) become convinced he'll be unfaithful

Q. 7 – Your partner works with some attractive female colleagues. When he says he's working late, do you assume:

(a) he's working late

(b) he's working late with his attractive colleague in a near-empty building

(c) he's gone to dinner with his attractive colleague

(d) he's in bed with his attractive colleague

(e) you are parked in a secluded area outside his workplace, waiting to see him leave with the attractive colleague

Q. 8 – You find an earring or other female evidence in his jacket pocket. Do you:

(a) think nothing of it

(b) confront him with it calmly

(c) hide it somewhere and harbour suspicions

(d) burst into tears

(e) fly into a rage and accuse him of having an affair

Q. 9 – Your partner puts a picture of some luscious babe on his wall or in his wallet. Do you:

(a) tease him for being like a teenager

(b) turn your nose up at such immature behaviour

(c) ignore it

(d) sulk until he takes it down/out

(e) voice your displeasure in no uncertain terms

Q. 10 – You run into him accidentally one day. He is with a group of people including some girls. Do you:

(a) introduce yourself with a beaming smile

(b) wait to be introduced

(c) pull him to one side and ask who they all are

(d) pull him to one side and cause a fuss

(e) make some excuse so he leaves the group to spend time with you

How did you score?

1. a = 2; b = 2; c = 3; d = 4; e = 5
2. a = 1; b = 0; c = 3; d = 2; e = 4
3. a = 0; b = 2; c = 3; d = 1; e = 4
4. a = 0; b = 1; c = 2; d = 3; e = 4
5. a = 0; b = 1; c = 4; d = 2; e = 3
6. a = 1; b = 0; c = 2; d = 3; e = 4
7. a = 0; b = 1; c = 2; d = 3; e = 4
8. a = 0; b = 1; c = 2; d = 3; e = 4
9. a = 0; b = 2; c = 1; d = 3; e = 4
10. a = 0; b = 1; c = 2; d = 3; e = 4

40 +

The Rack

It's a brave guy that will put up with this level of scrutiny and obsession. This is a worryingly high score and is the profile of someone who is either addicted to passionate scenes of break-up and make-up, or is seriously lacking in self-esteem. You need to cultivate a calmer approach to relationships otherwise you will scare your lovers away. With a woman on their case to this extent, most guys will be running for the hills. You have been watching too many soap operas and need to remember that jealousy in action is extremely uncivilised! Please try to talk to a professional counsellor about your problem, as few men will put up with your antics. And all bunnies in the area will be running for cover!

30–39

The Thumbscrews

You certainly like to wear the trousers – and wield the whip – in your relationships. Do you just not trust men per se, or is it your particular partner of the moment? Has he done anything to make you think he is unfaithful? If not, then you should learn to relax and remember that no one will thank you for assuming the worst of them. The level of suspicion you are demonstrating does not make for a healthy relationship and you should perhaps try to talk about your fears with a counsellor. You must be terribly tense a lot of the time, expecting the worst to happen. Sometimes, letting go is a fantastic relief.

16–29

The Raised Eyebrow

Well, you certainly like to know what your boyfriend is up to, but you are sensible enough to realise that giving him the third degree or sulking won't endear you to him. You are cautiously optimistic and will give him a long leash to enjoy himself, but you will still be able to rein him in if he starts taking liberties with your affection. You have a realistic idea of what men are like – that they think with their dicks most of the time – and you are wise to keep an eye on your other half. However, you are trusting and savvy enough to not worry unduly unless your antennae are activated by something really being amiss.

0–15

The Day Off

You are decidedly cool. You have such a grounded sense of your own self-worth that you aren't going to waste precious time worrying about what might or might not be going on in someone else's mind. You are happy in your own skin, content to let things take a natural course. If your guy is not answering his phone, you are not going to text him twenty times in one hour; you will get on with your life and be happy when he does call.

What about him?

Q. 11 – You sign up for a part-time college course. Does he:

    (a) express delight that his girlfriend is bettering herself

    (b) sulk

    (c) moan that you will probably meet some new hunk

    (d) barely register interest

    (e) insist on meeting you after class each week

Q. 12 – An ex-boyfriend shows up at a social event. What would be your partner's reaction?

    (a) he's already friends with him, so no problem

    (b) he wouldn't be too bothered

    (c) he would probably watch you closely all evening

    (d) he would leave in a huff

    (e) he would be aggressive to him

Q. 13. You're not at home one night when you say you are going to be. Does he:

    (a) not notice, he didn't call anyhow

    (b) call your mobile and chat generally

    (c) text you until you reply

    (d) demand an explanation of why you 'lied'

    (e) fly into a rage

Q. 14 – It's a girls' night out on the town. Does he:

  (a) tease you about your possible behaviour

  (b) arrange a lads' night out in another part of town

  (c) text you through the evening

  (d) insist on meeting up with you later

  (e) sulk and assume you are going on the pull

Q. 15 – You confess to having sexual fantasies about someone else. Does he:

  (a) tease you about it for fun

  (b) sulk

  (c) say he'll kill them

  (d) talk about his own fantasies

  (e) assume you are sleeping with this person

Q. 16 – You get promoted, but it will mean longer hours. What's his reaction?

  (a) he is delighted for you

  (b) he's disappointed that he won't see as much of you

  (c) he's unfazed by anything

  (d) he's suspiciously unimpressed and sulky

  (e) he's annoyed

Q. 17 – In a social situation, a man pays you a compliment about your appearance. Does he:

  (a) tease you about it

  (b) take it as a compliment to him that he has such a tasty girlfriend

  (c) seem unbothered

(d) accuse you of flirting

(e) start a ruck

Q. 18 – Has he ever gone through your personal stuff such as diary, emails, texts, etc.?

(a) never – it wouldn't occur to him

(b) you doubt it

(c) once or twice he has quizzed you as to your movements

(d) he's often asking who's calling you

(e) you have caught him – he doesn't trust you at all

Q. 19 – What's his body language when you are together in company?

(a) loving and warm

(b) friendly and casual

(c) distanced and formal

(d) slightly protective

(e) bristling and macho

Q.20 – Tick as many as apply:

(a) you dread parties with him cos he's always watching your every move

(b) much of the time you are together he is sulking

(c) he has accused you of seeing someone else, on the flimsiest of reasons

(d) he quizzes you about male colleagues

(e) he has told you that no one else will put up with you

How does he score?

11. a = 0; b = 2; c = 3; d = 1; e = 4
12. a = 0; b = 1; c = 2; d = 3; e = 4
13. a = 0; b = 1; c = 2; d = 3; e = 4
14. a = 0; b = 1; c = 2; d = 3; e = 4
15. a = 0; b = 2; c = 3; d = 1; e = 4
16. a = 0; b = 1; c = 2; d = 3; e = 4
17. a = 0; b = 1; c = 2; d = 3; e = 4
18. a = 0; b = 1; c = 2; d = 3; e = 4
19. a = 0; b = 1; c = 2; d = 3; e = 4
20. a = 2; b = 2; c = 3; d = 3; e = 4

42+

What an ogre!

Why are you giving yourself a hard time hanging out with this misery? You surely can't relax with him making notes about your every move. This man is no fun – it's official. Unless you are deep into a committed relationship and are helping him to overcome his considerable social skills problems, I would make a disappearing act. As Paul Simon said, 'there are fifty ways to leave your lover'. Seriously, life is too short to be beholden to someone in this way, treading on eggshells in case you shatter a fragile personality. There are some tips in the following section that explain such possessive behaviour.

26–41

What an effort!

Well, he's not an ogre, but he certainly has you on a short rein. Keeping him placated and assured that you are not about to run off with the nearest hunk must sometimes feel like a full-time job. Depending on how long you have been going out with this man, take a long cool look at the pros and cons. Does being with him make you happy? This is not the same as loving him. There is little reward or joy in loving someone deeply but not being able to enjoy your own life for fear of upsetting another person. If you know deep inside that his behaviour is not reasonable, if you ever feel tearful and emotionally exhausted from his constant worrying, remember that you don't have to suffer. Take a hike!

11–25

What a charmer!

This charming man will cherish you and want you to be happy. He doesn't need to keep a constant check on you in order to feel secure but he likes to know where he stands. He won't tolerate any deceit. He is also someone who is not beset by emotional insecurities and he doesn't want to hang around with people who are in any way neurotic. He has a highly developed sense of self-worth and will not be impressed by a partner who either runs herself down or takes him for granted. He will work with you, and together you will have a lot of fun built on mutual respect.

0–10

What a sweetie!

You have no worries with this laid-back dude. In fact, you could probably have a steamy affair with his best friend, in his house, and he wouldn't notice. OK, that may be an exaggeration, but here's a guy who will not want to cause an ugly scene in even the most provocative of circumstances. He is not given to emotional outbursts of any kind and is happy doing his own thing. He will be a real softie at heart, though, and once he's woken up from his chill out zone, he will be the most romantic of lovers.

GREEN-EYE SOLUTIONS

As I mentioned previously, jealousy is born out of low self-esteem or fear. The realisation that we have a problem is sometimes a lesson that can be learned only by scaring a couple of partners away. It is then that we can begin to develop new behavioural patterns, rather than sticking to the hair-trigger reactions that have become natural to us and are so unappealing. There is a latent neediness at the root of all jealous people; they will try to control everything around them that acts as a potential threat to their latest acquisition: their partner. One usually finds that, somewhere along the line, the jealous person was abandoned in some way as a child, or was never rewarded, or had something taken away from them. At the bottom line, they never got the attention they needed at a vulnerable time and consistently try to compensate for this loss in their adult life. An adult partnership can seem to fill that loss, covering up the emotional vacuum of unresolved abandonment. But unless the original source of the loss is addressed, the new partnership won't be enough. The jealous person will never be able to relax because he will live in a state of perpetual unconscious insecurity.

Most young people are naturally unpredictable, and will be resistant to the routine a jealous person will try to impose on them. (Think of how older partners are often portrayed as being over-protective of their 'acquisition'.) Consequently, a young jealous person will stand out from his peers even more than an older person with this affliction, making him seem even more 'uncool'. There will be many things that will threaten the jealous person's 'prop'. The jealous person needs to do everything he can to control the variables that will leave him exposed and lonely. Hence: checking their partner's email, diaries and phone calls. This is not an uncommon condition and, although it will seem like an insult if you are affected by someone's behaviour in this way, it is not done consciously to annoy you. It is totally about their own obsession with security.

Insecurities in men are often manifest by a controlling or dominating personality. In women, they are revealed through martyrdom, with the woman soliciting sympathy whenever she gets the chance. Some people just cannot help themselves from playing up to get attention; feigning the stomach ache so they have to leave the party early, or looking for ways to make sure their partner doesn't have fun without them. The jealous person will not be able to bear the thought of not being involved in their partner's good times. Sex, of course, will be a minefield of potentially volatile situations. In order to have fulfilling love lives, we need to relax, which the jealous person finds almost impossible to do. My advice would be to avoid getting in too deep with someone who is affected in this way unless they are prepared to admit they have a problem. They will suck you of energy and harbour resentments. They will need to slowly work towards independent, happy autonomy, but this is often only achieved through working on one's self or through therapy. The person with the problem has to tackle it for themselves and cannot be 'cured' merely by a sympathetic lover. In fact, appeasing their neuroses may delay change. If your jealous partner can at least admit there is a problem, and that their problem is rooted in their own history and not your behaviour, you will have something to work with together. If you do take on such a challenge, always remember to protect yourself from the negative influence of others. Don't let anybody stop you from having good times!

HOW TO SPOT A DYSFUNCTIONAL LOVER

Not all of us are lucky enough to grow up in households where we are nurtured and treated with respect and love. Some people have never known what it's like to feel safe and secure and have been able to gain attention only by lashing out. If you find yourself becoming sexually involved with a person who has difficulty controlling their anger, you need to be careful. You might be the first person to have ever shown them affection. And if you do anything by your actions that they could perceive as abandonment, you may have to witness their demons at close range. If one day you have a nasty surprise – that your new lover has anger-management issues – you need to withdraw carefully and calmly. You must work out according to your intuition what is 'healthy' anger and what is unreasonable aggression. You need to canvass the opinion of your friends and family and you may have to make a tough but ultimately sensible decision. An unreasonably aggressive partner will hook his claws into you and want to know your every move. He will impose increasingly impossible demands on you and you will find yourself 'treading on eggshells' to ensure you don't upset him. Before you know it, you will find yourself feeling responsible for his happiness and dancing to his tune.

Obviously there are varying degrees of damaged behaviour; we all know the shocking statistics about domestic violence. Yet many men do not need to lay a hand on their partners to cause them distress. Many of us can find ourselves in relationships that are psychologically damaging; where a partner is making unreasonable demands or being manipulative to the point of control-freakery. This is when your lover is a loser. I don't mean that he is on a low wage or isn't a high-flyer. I mean that he doesn't know the basic rules of respect. Being a loser is not about economics; it is about lacking the necessary empathy to recognise that you are being unreasonable and are not relating to others in a healthy way. So many women end up protecting men who aren't worth a hair on their heads – guys who are damaged goods; who want an easy ride and someone to clear up their mess for them. Do not make excuses to yourself. If he wants to use you as a meal-ticket, landlady, emotional punchbag, surrogate mother or chew-toy just get out of there, girl!

Every young woman should be given this information on her sixteenth birthday as most women, at some point in their lives, will come into contact with a dysfunctional man. If you are a grounded, sensible individual who has her antennae finely tuned to spot Trouble with a capital T, then you are blessed, and you will steer yourself around the offending obstacle and zoom off. Many women, unfortunately, are easily charmed by a wolf in sheep's clothing, and do not realise their mistake until they are already being sucked of money, time and energy by someone who is giving nothing back. Guys like this don't come with a government health warning; they aren't necessarily ugly, unintelligent, violent, or have criminal records. They can even be appealing, seeming somewhat vulnerable and loveable as they flatter you into accepting them closer into your life. But be wary; do not end up 'sleeping with the enemy'!

25 WARNING SIGNS THAT YOUR NEW MAN MAY BE DYSFUNCTIONAL

1. You have just met and he's borrowing money from you – like, more than £30.

2. He won't tell you his address.

3. He wants to leave loads of stuff at yours.

4. He wants to spend longer than you are comfortable with hanging out at yours.

5. He tries to dominate what should be mutual decisions: choice of movie, meals, meeting time and place, etc.

6. He isn't polite to waitresses or bar staff.

7. He leers at other women in your company.

8. His interest wanders when you are telling him something important about yourself.

9. He goes off to make lots of personal calls in your company, and won't tell you to whom.

10. He is alcohol- or drug-dependent or has gambling problems.

11. He has confessed to hurting animals.

12. He shows road rage way beyond the occasional expletive.

13. He criticises the way you clean/cook/dress/wash, etc. beyond the point of being 'a bit fussy'.

14. All of his mates seem dodgy.

15. He began the relationship by elevating you to an unrealistic, goddess-like status.

16. He bought you inappropriate gifts within the first couple of weeks of your knowing him.

17. He has children by different mothers he hardly sees.

18. He lives on junk food alone.

19. His personal hygiene is lacking.

20. He doesn't engage with common courtesies: please, thank you, etc.

21. He doesn't seem to be interested in your aspirations.

22. He has wild mood swings.

23. He gets into fights.

24. He obsesses about where you are and what you have been doing all day.

25. He goes crazy if he can't reach you immediately on your mobile.

Do not think that you can change the problem person that has attached himself to you, no matter how cute-looking or nice underneath he is. Maybe it's not his fault that he is in a bad situation right now, or that his dad beat him up as a kid or that his former girlfriend was a bitch, but it certainly isn't yours. There is being down on your luck and there is being a dysfunctional user. Being hard-up financially does not mean someone has to take advantage of others. If you do have the misfortune to meet someone who starts to show any of these traits, take a clear-headed critical assessment of the situation. Ask your friends their honest opinion and listen to their advice. If we have found ourselves in an abusive relationship, it is only natural to tell ourselves that things will improve. Unfortunately, unless that person acknowledges there is a problem and actually seeks counselling, he will not change. A man doesn't have to physically attack you for a relationship to be abusive. You may realise that over the course of a few months he has increased his criticism of you to a point that is making you feel really low, or that your friends make excuses to not be wherever he is because he has a reputation for 'going off on one'. Domestic or relationship abuse cuts across all social backgrounds but, whatever walk of life the abuser comes from, the problem is always inevitably rooted in that unholy trio of low self-esteem, resentment and fear. It is the nature of the person with the problem to project these qualities onto the nearest vulnerable party so that the person on the receiving end is chipped away at until they are questioning their own worth, status and sanity, soaking up all the problems until they become their own. I have heard the same story a thousand times from women who think they can change these poor miserable brutes. Their dysfunction is like a parasite that will feed upon the nearest warm and willing host. Do not let it happen to you!

THE WAY TO HEALTHY RELATIONSHIPS

We should feel happy with the sexual part of ourselves and have the courage of our erotic convictions. Yet we only need look at the many problem pages and relationship counselling that exists to realise that many of us are tormented by doubts about ourselves or the fidelity of our partners. Running a fun, healthy relationship is not as easy as we are led to believe, and it takes work. Those happy cheery people in the DIY ad all too easily turn into the brawling couple on *Trisha* or *Jerry Springer*. We need to spring-clean and maintain our love lives as we do our domestic life.

The better we know our erotic needs and desires, the better equipped we will be in dealing with the hiccups. Relationships have to be about give and take. Awareness is the name of the game, and it's good to cultivate flexibility when we find ourselves in conflict with our partners. Remember that each of us is an autonomous individual. No one else is responsible for your happiness but yourself. Although the behaviour of others can wound us emotionally, we need to cultivate an atmosphere of mutual respect in our relationships. By answering the questions in this book and thinking more deeply about the erotic part of ourselves, you should ideally have gained more insight into your sexual psyche – the unique blueprint for pleasure. If you have just met someone and are considering taking your sexual relationship further, you need to ask yourself whether you think you will be able to trust them with that blueprint. Do you want them to become acquainted with what's in the mix – so they can give you the kind of stimulation we are all entitled to? The perfect recipe for sexual satisfaction is absolute honesty, absolute trust and absolutely the right sense of fun. These four elements form the blueprint for loving, healthy, sexy relationships:

(i) **self-knowledge** – knowing why particular things arouse us

(ii) **erotic know-how** – having the courage to say what arouses us

(iii) **sensitivity** – being aware of our partner's likes and dislikes

(iv) **trust** – knowing that we won't be punished or laughed at for vocalising what arouses us

With these things in mind, I wish you fantastic, life-affirming, orgasmic times.